AGATE

MICROSTRUCTURE AND POSSIBLE ORIGIN

TERRY MOXON

Terra Publications

British Library Cataloguing-in-publication data

A catalogue record for this book is available from the British Library
ISBN 0 9528512 0 2

Published by Terra Publications, 55 Common Lane, Auckley, Doncaster, S.Yorks. DN9 3HX

First published 1996

Printed and bound by Antony Rowe Ltd., Chippenham, Witshire

Front Cover. Jasper agate, Burn Anne, Kilmarnock. A multi-variation in crystallisation produces this surreal effect. (x 100, crossed polars).

Rear Cover. Burn Anne agate.The yellow spots vary in size and influence the overall colour within the band. (x 100, plane polarised light).

Acknowledgements

Over the past twenty years, I have received help from many friends and colleagues. Interest in agate genesis started as the result of a combined investigation with Tony Robinson on the immiscibility of polyester resins. Some of these observed effects have been described in Chapter 5 and the joint development of the banding techniques is gratefully acknowledged.

Dr Derek Humphries gave much guidance and supervised my research into agate genesis at the Department of Geology, Sheffield University. During the same period, I was given expert instruction on the TEM by Harry Brockley. My knowledge of photomicroscopy was greatly enhanced by frequent discussions with the late Jack Houghton.

I am grateful to the Department of Earth Sciences, Cambridge University and in particular to Professor I. N. McCave who kindly gave me permission to carry out research on aged silica gels; Drs Andrew Putnis and Chris Jeans were pillars of wisdom in numerous discussions; Tony Abrahams explained the intricacies of X-ray diffraction techniques.

John Greenaway played the role of interested reader and kindly commented on the typescript. He suggested a number of improvements that have been acted upon but, as usual, any deficiencies in the text are my responsibility. I am grateful to Chris du Feu and Stephen Moxon for the computer drawn text figures. Eric Dunn designed and constructed a highly efficient lap grinding system.

Any attempt to unravel the story of agate genesis is made doubly difficult for the non-German reader. Prior to 1960, most of the scientific interest was with German petrologists and German literature, before this time, was often published without an English abstract. I am indebted to Dr Gert Schmid who, by helping with translations over a three year period, prevented the task from becoming monumental.

I have collected many agates on my frequent visits to Scotland but there is no doubt that the study has been greatly enhanced by the gift of material from John Raeburn. I am particularly indebted for the samples of the rare and beautiful Burn Anne agate.

Finally, thanks are due to my wife Chris, children Stephen and Yvonne who have put up with my obsession with Mistress Agate *(such a beautiful gemstone could only be female!)* over the past twenty years.

Contents

Introduction

Agates are made from the two major elements in the earth's crust: silicon (Si) and oxygen (O). When the silicon and oxygen combine directly they do so in a number ratio of 1:2, producing silica with the chemical formula SiO_2. Quartz is the most common form of silica and constitutes an estimated 12% by volume of the earth's crust. Clear, crystalline quartz is known as rock crystal but the typical quartz garden pebbles are often milky, due to the presence of a multitude of small **inclusions**. The rarer coloured forms of **macroquartz** appear to owe their colour to the distribution of metallic **ions**: the purple in amethyst and the pale pink colour in rose quartz are thought to be caused by trace iron.

Chalcedony, agate, **chert**, flint and jasper are examples of micro-crystalline quartz that only reveal their true crystalline nature when sections are ground down to transparency and examined with a polarising microscope. Distinctions between these types depend upon their microtexture. However, divisions are not always clear but chert, flint and jasper are predominantly granular with chert grading into jasper as the impurities, particularly iron oxide, increase. Chalcedony and agate show a fibrous microstructure with the colour in chalcedony being distributed uniformly, whereas in agate the colour is arranged in bands.

Agates can be found throughout the world occupying gas cavities and veins in basalt rocks whose age can be tens of millions to hundreds of millions of years old. Whole fresh agates generally retain a slightly pitted, greenish appearance and are more resistant than the host rock to weathering. Transportation by sea and glacial action, millions of years after formation, results in a smoother appearance with the hard agates frequently surviving while the softer **igneous** rock is destroyed.

Igneous rocks are formed when the **magma** (*a thick paste of crystals, liquid and gas*) crystallises on, or beneath, the earth's surface. The rock type depends upon the parent magma and the rate of cooling but agate is to be found only in **basalt** and **andesite**. These basic lavas are low in silica erupting gently and flowing easily. Dissolved gases rise on the release of the initial retaining pressure. The composition of these volatile components varies with water vapour and carbon dioxide in a high proportion but lethal concentrations of sulphur dioxide, chlorine and hydrogen fluoride make the collection of gases a hazardous activity. Many gases escape but as the outer lava layer cools some of the gas bubbles are trapped.

The upper layer of the lava flow is often slaggy in appearance and where multiple lava flows have occurred these frothy lava tops are good indicators for the beginning and end of the different flows. Typically, the agates are to be found in the middle to lower half of the lava flow occupying the original **vesicles** (*gas cavities*) that were first trapped by the molten lava millions of years ago.

Lapidary magazines and journals use a proliferation of descriptive terms for this cheap and attractive gemmological material. The mineral is found mainly as an infilling of cavities in an igneous environment and in this book, agate types have been limited to fortification, horizontally banded and vein agate. Fortification agate is banded chalcedony whose pattern is reminiscent of a sectioned onion while horizontally banded agate shows a pattern of horizontal bands in all or part of the cross section, both types are to be found as **geodes** (*cavity fillings*). Fissure filling produces a third type: vein agate.

The last detailed review of the problems of agate genesis, in English, was in 1927 (Farrington). It is hoped that the geologist, mineral collector and general reader will find areas of interest within the text. References are given on page 93 and readers can order photocopies of specific papers from the British Library via their local library.

Technical terms are printed in **bold** and explained in the Glossary on page 101.

Chapter 1 The agate-bearing lava in the Midland Valley, Scotland

In the United Kingdom, the Midland Valley, Scotland is the major source of agate and it is to be found mainly in the **andesites** and **basalts** of **Devonian** age but excluded from similar Scottish lavas of **Carboniferous** age. Agates do occur in the Carboniferous olivine basalts of Derbyshire (Wray, 1954) and agates have been found in the Tertiary lavas on the south coast of Mull (Richey, 1961). England and Wales are virtually free of native agate apart from those in the Derbyshire basalts and the Devonian andesites of the Cheviots. Agates that have been found in England are predominantly the result of glacial action and longshore drift.

The Midland Valley is an ancient rift valley approximately 120 miles in length and 50 miles wide with boundaries defined by the fault lines running across Scotland from Greenock to Stonehaven and Ballantrae in Ayrshire to Dunbar (Fig.1.1). Today's principal agate localities in the Midland Valley still rely heavily on the explorations in the latter half of the eighteenth century by M.F.Heddle. Heddle was professor of chemistry at St. Andrews University and his book, *The Mineralogy of Scotland*, was published some four years after his death in 1901. The magazines and journals of the amateur mineral collector still quote these first published sites. However, modern transport and the popularity of collecting have meant that the extraction of agate from the lava has outpaced the natural erosive forces; finding agate in some reputed classic sites is very difficult today. Nevertheless, the chisel marks, empty hollows and agate remains are all indicative and, in part, the small unwanted agates have served this investigation equally well.

1.1 The western half of the Midland Valley

The occurrence of Devonian andesite is limited in Ayrshire and the Carrick Hills, Dunure is the largest outcrop. The author has examined three areas of lava flows and although the coastal stretches have fine exposures, the inland extensions are very limited. Only two outcrops are of sufficient size to warrant mention on O.S. sheet 70 (1:50 000, New Series). The Maidens, Turnberry section is a one and a half mile narrow strip of rock that is fully exposed along the coast. This section shows aspects that are also repeated in the Culzean and Carrick sections. Perhaps the most distinctive feature is the filling of fissures and hollows by a blue **mudstone** that acts as a cement for the large lava boulders that are up to three metres in diameter. Beds of red sandstone and mudstone are fine-grained which Tyrell (1913) and Smith (1910) cite as evidence for their original deposition in shallow pools.

The loss of iron by the lava is also shown by the **hematite** staining that covers a considerable area of the lava at sea level. The staining appears to penetrate to a depth of about 2 mm and can withstand erosion by the sea to a greater extent than the surrounding rock. Most small fissures, up to 3 m in length, are filled with **macroquartz** or agate or both minerals and quite frequently the first deposit in the vein is hematite. Sometimes, both iron oxide and silica have deposited together giving the agate a brown colouration.

The Carrick Hills have a very good coastal exposure lying in NNE direction from Drumshang to Bracken Bay: a distance of about three miles. Rock outcrops on the eastern side are few and mainly concentrated along the line from Drumshang Loch to White Craig which lies on a well-vegetated scarp outline. The rocks in these upper reaches are of a slaggy appearance but agate free. However, evidence of past **hydrothermal** activity emerged when a few **geodes** of smoky quartz were found in a burn and a fine amethyst quartz geode was removed from a rock fissure. Vegetation covers the upper western slopes and these have even fewer outcrops. The author did find samples of purple brown agate from a very friable lava near the radio mast on Brown Carrick. Towards the sea, the coarse grass changes to good quality farmland; the fields reportedly yield excellent agate during the winter months. A set of agates, all characterised by a purple hue, was collected from the lava at the top of Brown Carrick Hill to the lava at sea level. Dunure beach and the exposed rock to the north of the harbour are noted for their horizontally banded agate. Much of the agate is surrounded by an extremely brittle type of **chalcedony** and the attempts of previous collectors to remove the agate can be seen by the

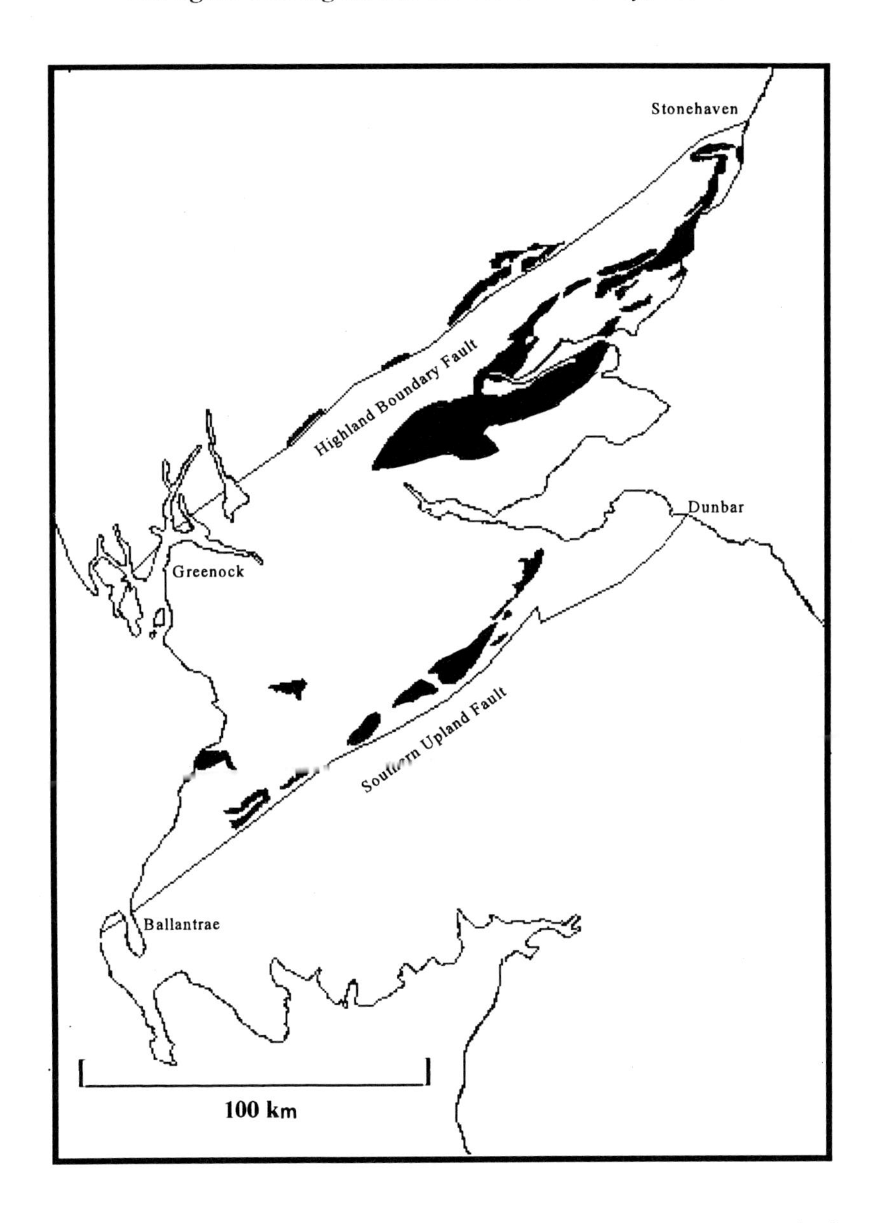

Fig.1.1 The Midland Valley within the Highland Boundary and Southern Upland fault lines.The dark areas are the Devonian outcrops.

fragments left in the rock. Some geodes have quartz centres up to 10 cm in diameter.

The construction of the Ayr to Girvan railway allowed Smith (1910) to collect many hundreds of agates and write the *Semi-Precious Stones of Carrick*. **Celadonite** (green earth) is described as the first formed mineral that lines the cavity wall and the mineral occurs with such frequency that Smith only comments on its absence. The mineral is usually present as no more than a wash on the outer surface of most fresh agates found in the Midland Valley. Generally, celadonite allows the agate to be removed from the surrounding rock when subject to the forces of man or nature. When celadonite is absent, then the adhesion between rock and agate is much greater. Two frequently occurring minerals described by Smith (1910) and Heddle (1901) are **opal** and cachalong. The latter is an intense, white, porcellanic mineral that adheres to the tongue but under the microscope reveals an opaque fibrous, chalcedonic structure. Opal has had a long history in hypotheses on agate genesis but the two authors are referring to the opaque white bands that are chalcedonic quartz.

The railway is now disused and overgrown. The author has investigated all exposures for many miles but there is now little evidence of the agate that Smith collected. A few areas had small agate samples up to 3 or 4 mm in diameter but the lack of previous activity is evident by the absence of chisel marks on the rock face.

The Straiton outcrops, with those at Galston near Kilmarnock, are the remaining Ayrshire andesite lavas of **Devonian** age. Some time was spent investigating the Straiton lavas enclosed by the Straiton, Tarlow and Straiton, Dalmellington roads. A few agates can be found in the scree slopes (Fig.1.2) but are rare in the nearby bedrock.

1.2 The eastern half of the Midland Valley

Perthshire is the source of many of Heddle's sites and his agates from the Blue Hole at Usan are on display in the National Museum, Edinburgh. The southern bank of the River Tay is a well-documented site of beach

Fig. 1.2 Agate nodules can be found on the scree slopes at Straiton.

agate. At Balmerino, the coastline consists of a shingle beach with a background of boulder clay; a single ten metre outcrop of lava was found that contained small translucent orange agates. A typical exposure on the Wormit to Tayport stretch has a height of about seven metres and is overhung with boulder clay. Larger specimens of blue-grey agate were found and much of the lava contained tiny agate fillings. I made short visits to two of Heddle's (1901) sites at Kinnoull Hill and Path of Condie but found little of interest.

A well-exposed escarpment extends down the Glen Rait valley and while the escarpment was free of agates, the nearby fields contain ample agate geodes and fragments. The field agates were all free from any celadonite coating and were translucent grey in bulk but in **thin section** the colour disappears to give a cloudy gel-like appearance. The white banding was faint and more usually the chalcedony apparently band-free. However, close examination of the **conchoidal** fractured samples showed a raised **fortification** pattern that resembled fingerprints with similar defined ridges.

Agate bearing lava is found both north and south of the Montrose basin. However, the coastal stretches have had much publicity over the years and it is predominantly beach agate that is found today. The coastal outcrop from Scurdie Ness Lighthouse to Boddin Point still contains

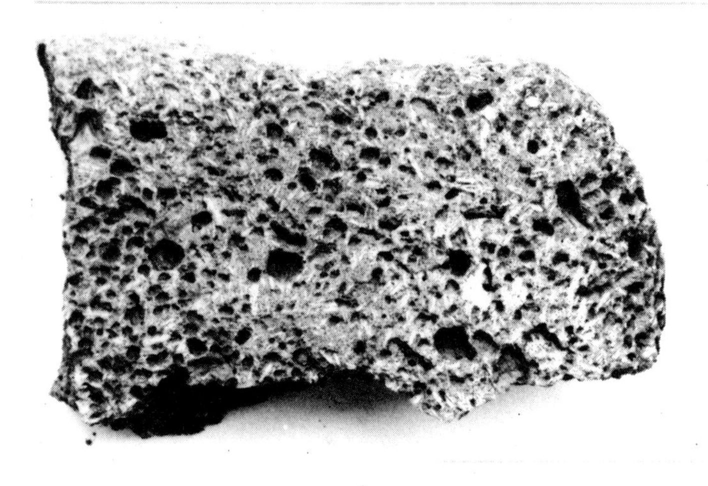

Fig.1.3 Vesicular lava. The dark patches are empty gas cavities and the thin needle-like crystals are feldspars. Path of Condie. One fifth size.

Fig.1.4 Cavity nodule. The larger amygdales have been filled with silica but the small upper nodule in the right block of lava contains celadonite. One fifth size.

specimens of agate but fractured samples show why they have been left by collectors: the additional calcite and **chlorite** detract from the delicate pale blue agates.

Mykura (1961) discussed the Devonian lavas in the Pentland Hills but made no mention of the silica minerals. My own excursions around Glencarse reservoir would confirm their absence. Although two samples of agate bearing lava were found, one, an erratic contained **feldspar phenocrysts** up to 2cm in length.

Macpherson (1989) has revised Heddle's original sites and the interested collector can see the beauty of Scottish agates in the coloured plates within the book. Alternatively, many specimens are on display at the National Museum, Edinburgh.

1.3 Petrology of the agate-bearing lavas.

Thin section slides have been made of more than thirty samples of agate-bearing lava from the Midland Valley. Given the widespread nature of the collection, the observations are monotonously similar. Feldspar phenocrysts are usually present but zoning is present in only four samples. Many phenocrysts show some alteration (Fig.1.5) but equally other samples contain perfectly fresh feldspars with andesine being the prominent **feldspar**.

Footnote: *The study of **igneous** rocks is a complex subject. Fundamentally, the cooling lava can produce major minerals with quartz, feldspars (sodium/ potassium/ calcium silicates) and ferromagnesian types (iron/ magnesium silicates) being the most prevalent. If the lava cools quickly, then fine-grained or even glassy rocks will form. Slow cooling allows large crystals to form. Some rocks will show evidence of a two stage crystallisation when larger first formed crystals (phenocrysts) are distinguished from the smaller and later formed crystals (groundmass).*

Fig. 1.5 The alteration in the feldspar is shown by the fine clay specks. Path of Condie.

Fig. 1.6 These feldspars crystals are are free from alteration. Dundee quarry.

The feldspars are the larger crystals and thin needle-like crystals in the glassy groundmass.Short edge of micrograph represents 4 mm. (x 14, crossed polars)

The **ferromagnesian** phenocrysts were all highly altered with faint ghosts common. Biotite was the most common ferromagnesian mineral from the Carrick Hills. Many appear as alteration products of orthpyroxene in view of the sections encountered. **Augite** and **orthopyroxene** both showed much alteration and the former was classified by its birefringence and extinction.

Feldspars in the groundmass followed the usual pattern with none more basic than the phenocrysts and generally were more acidic. The ferromagnesian minerals, when present, were in order of frequency biotite, augite and orthopyroxene. Generally they were not as heavily altered as their phenocryst counterparts. **Magnetite** dust was well scattered throughout most of the lava but the feature that characterised all of the thin sections was the high colour index that ranged from green-yellow to black with brown predominant. This andesitic glass occupies 25 to 50% of the total slide area and is amply evident in Figs. 1.5, 1.6.

Overall, the agate bearing lavas of the Midland Valley can be classified as glassy **andesites** or **basalts**.

Chapter 2 Rocks in thin section, equipment and techniques

The preparation of agate in **thin section** requires a microscope, diamond saw and a power driven lap. While the microscope must be purchased, the last two can be made relatively cheaply by the interested user. Some readers may have part of the equipment and this chapter describes how sections can be made outside the laboratory using home-made apparatus. Studies on rock thin sections would normally require a polarising microscope but, with a price of at least £700, it would be outside the budget range of any casual viewer. A simple conversion on a biological microscope is much cheaper and a reasonable second hand biological microscope can be obtained for less than £100. Professionally made rock thin sections have a surface area of at least 4 cm^2 and are ground down to a standard thickness of 0.03 mm. At this thickness, most minerals become transparent and, when sandwiched between a pair of crossed polaroids, show **interference colours** that help in the identification of minerals within the slide. The reader might consider making a simple polariscope that uses about £3 worth of polaroid.

2.1 Polariscope

A simple version of a polariscope is easily made with costs limited to the purchase of polaroid. The casing is made from a 35-mm film container and two small pieces of polaroid (Fig.2.1). Centrally drilled holes of ~15 mm and 20 mm are made in the bottom and in the moveable top of the container. Two pieces of polaroid (purchased from a laboratory supplier or photographic dealer) are cut and stuck inside the top and bottom of the holder. Slits need to be cut within 5 mm of the top of the tube and these must allow an easy passage of a thin section on a standard 76 x 26 mm microscope slide. The bottom polaroid is fixed and the upper polaroid can be twisted through 360°. When the two polaroids have their planes of vibration at right angles to each other, they produce darkness: the polars are said to be in the crossed or extinction position.

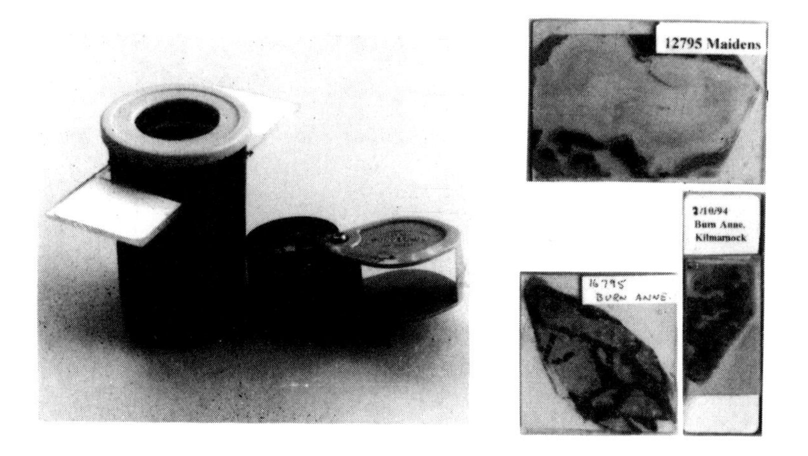

Fig. 2.1 A simple polariscope with slide and hand lens. Three useful sizes of slide are: 76 x 26 mm, 52 x 52 mm, 76 x 52 mm. The larger slides allow a greater area for comparing textures. However, these sections require more skill to make and are usually left thicker than the standard 0.03 mm.

Examination of thin sections should be carried out with the polaroids in this position. With polaroids adjusted to the crossed position, a thin section slide is passed through the slits. A hand lens is placed close to the eye and the polariscope is brought up to the hand lens while being pointed at a relatively strong source of light but not directly at the sun.

2.2 Converting a biological microscope into a polarising microscope

Many microscope manufacturers make polaroid fittings for their own range of microscopes. Again, these would be too expensive (~£25 +) for occasional use but the 35-mm film container tube from the polariscope allows the construction of a cheap holder for the upper polaroid dropped over the eye piece. The lower polaroid can sit in any available filter carrier. Otherwise, ingenuity is required to fit the polaroid below the stage. Purchasing separate polaroid for the microscope conversion is not necessary as the lower polaroid can be made from the top of the polariscope and fixed with Blu-Tack. For prolonged use, the converted microscope is less tiring on the eye than the polariscope and hand lens.

2.3 Preparation of rock slices in thin section

The principles of making rock thin sections are essentially the same as those first devised by Henry Sorby in 1849. A small rock fragment is ground flat, cleaned and the flattened face stuck onto a microscope slide. Grinding the exposed rock face reduces the thickness to a standard 0.03 mm. Actual measurements of the thickness are not made but are judged from the **interference colours** (see Appendix) of known minerals.

Grinding rocks by hand on glass or steel plates is possible. However, it is essential that a suitable rock is selected for this method. Any rock, eg **gypsum**, that can be cut with a hack saw would be suitable for a first attempt at making thin sections by hand. Unless time is unlimited, agate requires machine driven equipment.

Requirements.

i) Standard microscope slide (76 x 26 mm).
ii) Two part cold epoxy resin (eg Rapid Araldite).
iii) Silicon carbide (carborundum) grits 200, 400, 600 grade. Grits can be purchased from rock shops and held in separate, labelled pepper pots. 100 grade would be required for harder rocks.
iv) Two perfectly ground flat plates of steel or commercial glass (6 mm preferred but 4 mm is acceptable). Size ~ 25 x 20 cm. If glass plates are used, ***then the sharp edges must be removed*** either by the glazier or by the user with a carborundum stone. An alternative would be to permanently seal the edges with glued, flexible-spine material used for retaining A4 paper.
v) Two buckets half filled with water. These are to be used for washing the plates and slides. Use one bucket for coarse 100, **200** grit and the second for the fine 400, 600 grits. ***When the exercise is finished, the grits will set hard and should not be flushed down the sink***.
vi) Cover slips. The thin section can be covered with a glass cover slip. If cover slips are ordered, then purchase the more substantial No 2 at 32

x 22 mm. Temporary seals between the rock and cover slip can be made with clove or olive oil.

vii) Photocements (eg Loctite Glass Bond) are useful permanent adhesives for fixing the cover slips.

viii) A converted junior biological microscope. ***The grinding exercise is messy and using a cheap microscope for this purpose is advisable***; the grits and water would damage a quality microscope. The author uses a petrological microscope for serious study and a converted junior biological microscope (costing £40) for the preparation of thin sections.

ix) A suitable rock. Several texts on the subject infer that hand grinding can be carried out on most rocks. However, the harder rocks should be left until machine-driven equipment is available. A suitable rock for this exercise would be gypsum (or any rock that can be cut with a hack saw). However, gypsum as satin spar is too crumbly and should be avoided.

x) A pile of old newspaper, kitchen roll, old tooth brush, and clothes pegs.

xi) Safety glasses when grinding.

Preparation (~time for the stage is shown in brackets)

1) First stage:

a) Cut a thick section of gypsum (~ 30 x 20 x 3 or 4 mm) with a fine toothed hack saw. (~ **1 min**)

b) Place the glass or steel plate on a pile of newspaper. Add a small amount of water and 200 grit. Grind the face in a series of small circular motions until the saw marks have been removed. The newspaper can be regularly changed as it soaks up the grit slurry. (**~1min)**

c) Wash the slide and remove all **200** grit.

d) Repeat b) using the second plate and the 600 grit until the face is smooth. (**~1 min**)

e) Wash and ***thoroughly dry*** the rock. Mix sufficient epoxy to cover the flattened face and thinly coat that area at the centre of the slide. Place the flattened face on the slide, squeezing the rock and slide so that all the air bubbles are removed. Clamp the rock and slide longitudinally using two clothes pegs. (~ **2 min**). The set epoxy is harder than the gypsum and if excess resin is removed before it has hardened, then it does help the later grinding process.

Leave the slide undisturbed for 24 hours. If a few slides are made, then prepare all sections for each stage before moving on to the next stage. About four rocks can be stuck before the epoxy starts to set.
(**Total preparation time / slide ~ 5 min**)

2) Second stage:

Requirements
i) Two plates, glass or steel ii) Polariscope or, preferably, a converted biological microscope (but note the previous warning at requirements viii).

a) Repeat stage b) from the first stage until the rock ***becomes near transparent***. The rock section will now be about 0.2 mm thick (gypsum, approximately 3 mm thick, would take about **8 min** to reach 0.2 mm). Thoroughly wash away all traces of 200 grit.

b) Repeat stage d) first stage and use the microscope, with the polaroids in the extinction position, to judge the thickness. Tear a sheet of kitchen roll and place on a newspaper. Remove most of the grit slurry from the slide via the bucket of water and give a final rinse with tap water from a wash bottle. Place the slide face up on the kitchen roll sheet to remove the bulk of the water. If a polariscope has to be used, it should be pointed downwards towards the light source so that drips of water are not falling on the viewer. ***The secret for making a good slide is constantly to check and ensure even wear.*** It does require considerable skill to produce a quality slide and it might be preferable to cease grinding when the crystals start to show very pale pastel shades of purple and green (**variable ~ 7 min**). At this point, the section is thick but the crystal detail is clear. However, the later stages are very exciting and much pleasure can be obtained by watching the changes in the interference colours (Appendix)

The final grinding stages produce very strong orange, then yellow, then green, then blue to red. Further grinding would give an orange yellow colour when the section is approximately 0.06 mm and white if the standard 0.03 mm is reached. ***However, at the standard thickness of 0.03***

mm, the rock is almost ready for total removal from the slide. If an alternative to gypsum has been selected, then the final interference colour at 0.03 mm is likely to be different.

c) After grinding has finished, the slide can be well washed in soapy water and gently scrubbed with an old tooth brush. (**1 min**)

d) The slide should be thoroughly dried and the rock section ***sparingly*** coated with photocement and protected by the glass cover slip. The base of an old ball point pen can be used to press gently on the cover slip to remove air bubbles and make good rock contact. Press too hard and the cover slip will crack. (**2 min**). These cements require UV light to set and must be either left outside or cured with a UV lamp.

Temporary seals between the cover slip and rock can be made with a few drops of olive oil. If cover slips are not on hand, then protection of the objective (*lower*) lens can be achieved by using a second microscope slide. However, the lens system of a quality microscope will have been corrected for use with the correct size of cover slip and these must be used for high magnification observations. There is much to be seen at around 20 x magnification and the double slide thickness is not too much of a problem at low magnifications.

2.4 Machine cutting and grinding

---

a) Rock saw

Enthusiastic collectors may already have a diamond rock saw, in which case the equipment can be used to produce a slice of rock ~ 30 x 25 x 2 mm. For the reader who has never used a diamond saw then the following brief description applies to the author's homemade 6" trim saw (Fig 2.2). The power unit is a 1/4 hp motor from an old domestic washing machine linked to the saw spindle via pulleys and a car fan belt. The saw spindle is supported by ball bearing plummer blocks fixed to Dexion-type angle iron. After passing through a plastic Adis tank, the spindle holds the blade sandwiched between two 2" flanges ***(these are essential for blade support)*** and locked by two nuts. A 3 mm thick perspex lid, containing

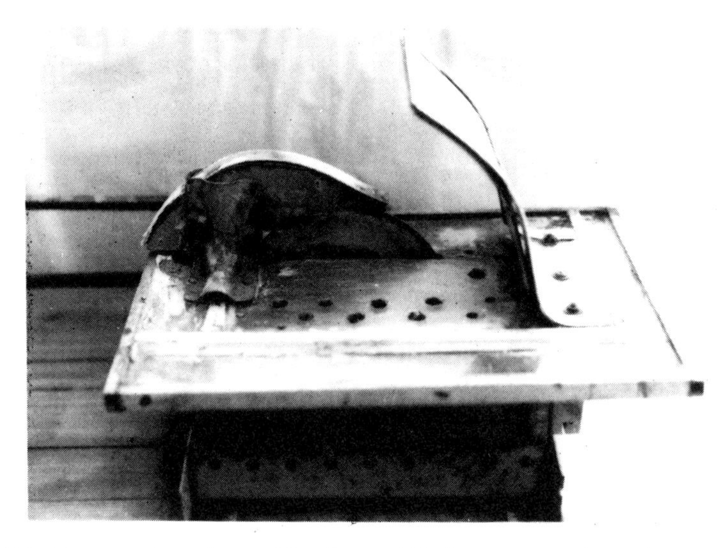

Fig. 2.2 Home-made rock saw. The diamond blades are expensive and to prevent rusting they should be removed immediately after use.

Fig.2.3 A rock grinding lap with the protection covering removed to show the pulley gearing.

multiple drill holes, is hinged to the wooden side supports on the tank. Dirty coolant with rock flour requires frequent tank cleaning and the use of Dexion angle iron runners assists dismantling.

Trim saws do allow the rock to be hand-held but the blade must run in a suitable tank coolant. A full splash canopy is not used for this saw but it is essential that the operator is protected from the coolant by a partial guard over the blade. A splash guard protects the operator from coolant by retaining the forward spray. 1:1 gearing allows the blade spindle to turn at the speed of the motor: 1425 rpm. At this speed, it is inevitable that fine mists of coolant are produced and this author does not wish to inhale droplets of the oil-based coolants. Tap water plus a little washing up liquid is all that is used when cutting rock materials -including agate.

A diamond blade is the one item that even the most competent engineer would need to purchase. Modern blades are steel discs impregnated with diamond and they cut by grinding. Unless the blade has been damaged, it does not have any sharp cutting edges. Eventually, the diamond edge of the blade will become glazed and needs to be sharpened by cutting a few slices off a carborundum stone. Retain the coolant in the tank when de-glazing the blade.

b) Grinding Lap

There are many variations of a simple lap but the amateur lapidary should note that the small, centre bolt lap that is useful for producing flat slabs of stone is unacceptable for preparing thin sections. The centre bolt gets in the way and there is insufficient grinding area. It is hoped that the following will provide some ideas for the construction of a suitable lap. One of the author's laps (shown in Fig. 2.3) is essentially a revolving iron disc (10" x 0.75") connected to a drive spindle that is, in turn, linked by pulleys to a 1/4 hp motor. The lap is geared by the pulleys (1:8) and fixed to a small plate by bolts. Alternatively, the lap could be screwed on to the top of a shaft that passes through a rectangular tank. Although there is a choice of a variety of tank materials, a plastic *Crystalware* washing up bowl is used for the open-topped slurry retaining tank. The use of plastic has saved many slides from breaking when they have been 'snatched' by the slurry and flung against the tank wall. One side of the bowl is drilled for a drain hole. A small tapered tube fills the hole and a rubber pipe leads waste water into a bucket. Support for the bottom of the bowl is achieved, in this case, by a steel shelf but angle iron has been used in the past. All drilled holes are made water proof by mastic sealant. Self-aligning, square based Plummer Blocks (ball bearing type) are used to brace the spindle and the unit is totally supported by Dexion angle iron and floor mounted.

The author's two laps are geared to operate at a nominal 180 rpm (1:8) and 23 rpm (1:8 and a further 1:8) but for many years the first named lap was used for all stages of machine grinding. However, if all grindings are to be carried out on a single lap, then the author would recommend a gearing that gave a speed of around 90 rpm. In principle, the grinding process is just a faster version of the method described in **2.3**. If the reader is totally unfamiliar with making rocks in thin section, then a quartz pebble would be an excellent starting point for initial practice. The diamond saw can be used to produce a slice of quartz ~ 30 x 25 x 2 mm. Squirt a small amount of water from a washing up liquid-type container and add 200 grit. Start grinding with a series of small circular motions and grind the slice flat on the lap. Check the surface in reflected light and when the surface is free from flaws, thoroughly clean the lap and switch to 400 grade grit and repeat the grinding process. Repeat with 600 grade grit. Clean the slice, dry and fix to the microscope slide as described in **2.3.**

Refer to the second stage **2.3** and carry out the grinding process with 200 grade grit until the quartz pebble shows transparency. Start to use the microscope as described in **2.3,** second stage a), until pale pastel shades appear. Clean the lap and switch to water and 400 grade grit. Repeat the process by grinding the rock until the grains produce a strong blue-green colour with the polars crossed. Thoroughly wash the slide and switch to a small amount of water with 600 grade grit on a glass plate. Delicate touches are required to achieve even thickness and frequent returns to the glass plate are essential. Continue the grinding process until the colour of the whole thin section, when viewed with the polars crossed, is straw yellow to white. The slide has been ground down to the standard thickness of 0.03mm. Well done!

It is inevitable that early efforts will produce problems: what was clearly visible one minute has totally disappeared the next; uneven grinding producing wedge cross sectioned slides and so on. Persevere, perhaps stopping before the standard thickness is reached as the crystal structure can still be observed with a thicker slide. Quartz has been selected for a first effort as it can be found in a reasonable pure state and the observer knows that the bulk of the slide contains mainly quartz crystals. Secondly, the same changes in interference colours will be found in agate: it is only the microstructure that changes.

Safety Note: Water and electricity do not mix. The user must ensure that all home-made equipment is safe.

Further Reading

Humphries, D.W. (1992) *The preparation of thin sections of rocks, minerals and ceramics*. RMS Microscopy Handbooks. No. 24. Royal Microscopical Society, Oxford University Press, Oxford.

The only book that this author has read dealing solely with techniques for making thin section slides. After reading the book, there will be few further questions that need to be asked.

Allman, M., Lawrence, D.F. (1972) *Geological laboratory techniques.* Blandford Press.

Primarily aimed at the University laboratory but there are several techniques described that are of interest to the amateur mineralogist.

Smith, H.G. (1976) *Minerals and the Microscope.* Murby, London.

An old text but it still contains material that is relevant for the beginner in microscopy and petrology.

Equipment Suppliers

Interested readers would be advised to ring for catalogue prices.

Pulleys, flanges, spindles, Plummer blocks and much more.

Picador Ltd., Foxhills Industrial Estate, Scunthorpe, S. Humberside. DN15 8QJ (01724 281305)

Diamond saw blades and grits.

Use the Yellow Pages (Lapidary Supplies)

Microscope Slides

Obtainable from all laboratory equipment suppliers (Yellow Pages). If damaged hands are to be avoided, do ensure that quality slides (eg Chance Proper) are bought and **all four sides of the slide have been sand blasted.**

1 box of 100 slides 76 x 26 mm.

1 box of 100 cover slips No 2, 32 x 22 mm.

Chapter 3 The microstructure of agate

a) b) c)

Fig. 3.1 a) jasper in thin section: the white grains are quartz, grey is red and yellow iron oxide, black areas are due to clay particles; b) banded flint with quartz grains just visible at this magnification, c) agate showing the fibrosity that has formed after crystallisation has started from a small spherulite. All micrographs x 18, a) and b) plane polarised light, c) crossed polars. Short edge represents 2.4 mm.

Chemical analyses, X-ray and electron diffraction techniques have allowed Flörke and co-workers (1991) to provide a detailed explanation of the structure of various silica minerals. However, the purpose of this chapter is to describe observations that can be made with the optical microscope and link these observations to the extra detail obtained by using the scanning and transmission electron microscope (SEM and TEM).

Thin sections of agate can be made using the machine techniques described in chapter 2. Agate is exceptionally hard and its compact microstructure does mean that even when cut with a rock saw, ground on an electrically driven lap, a single thin section can take about 90 minutes to prepare. Ruining a slide is so easy. This always seems to happen at the later stages of slide making; the beginner would be well advised to master the basic skills before starting to attempt making thin sections of agate. However, even a wedged shaped section or one that is starting to feather badly at the edges will show interesting detail that is worth further study. Persevere and your skills will develop.

Under the microscope, the microcrystalline quartz minerals have been generally classified according to their textures with **chert** and flint being predominantly granular. **Chalcedony** and agate show a fibrous structure as the major textural form (Fig. 3.1). Each agate produces unique banding and it therefore follows that each agate thin section will be different. After an examination of a few hundred slices of agate in thin section, it is suggested that there are many variations to be included in the term **petrographic fibrosity**. The major structural types are shown in Fig. 3.2.

3.1 Textures in agate under the polarising microscope

Textures based upon the long fibres

a) Fibres. The typical chalcedonic quartz with radiating bundles of fibres that can reach hundreds of microns in length ($1 \mu m = 10^{-6}$ m). These textural appearances range from very fine to coarse; the latter resembling iron filings under the influence of a magnetic field.

b) Wavy fibres. Wave forms are revealed as bands superimposed on coarse fibres and are shown with interference colours at a higher order than the background.

c) Sheaf. Fibres can be arranged as a distinct sheaf structure that is often the start of a growth leading to type a).

d) Fan. Thin fibrous forms can arrange in the shape of a fan.

Textures based upon the spherulite

e) Spherulite. The true spherulite is rare in agate and when found is usually surrounded by a texturally different form.

f) Rosette is a very common texture growing from a single point in a radial direction.

g) Fan rosette is a combination of types d) and f).

Granular and feather textures

h) Granular. The appearance of granules of quartz in agate is not rare. A decrease in the grain size produces a dusty appearance.

Fig.3.2 Observed microtextures of agate when the polaroids are in the crossed position. The magnification is variable but within the 15 to 65 x range.

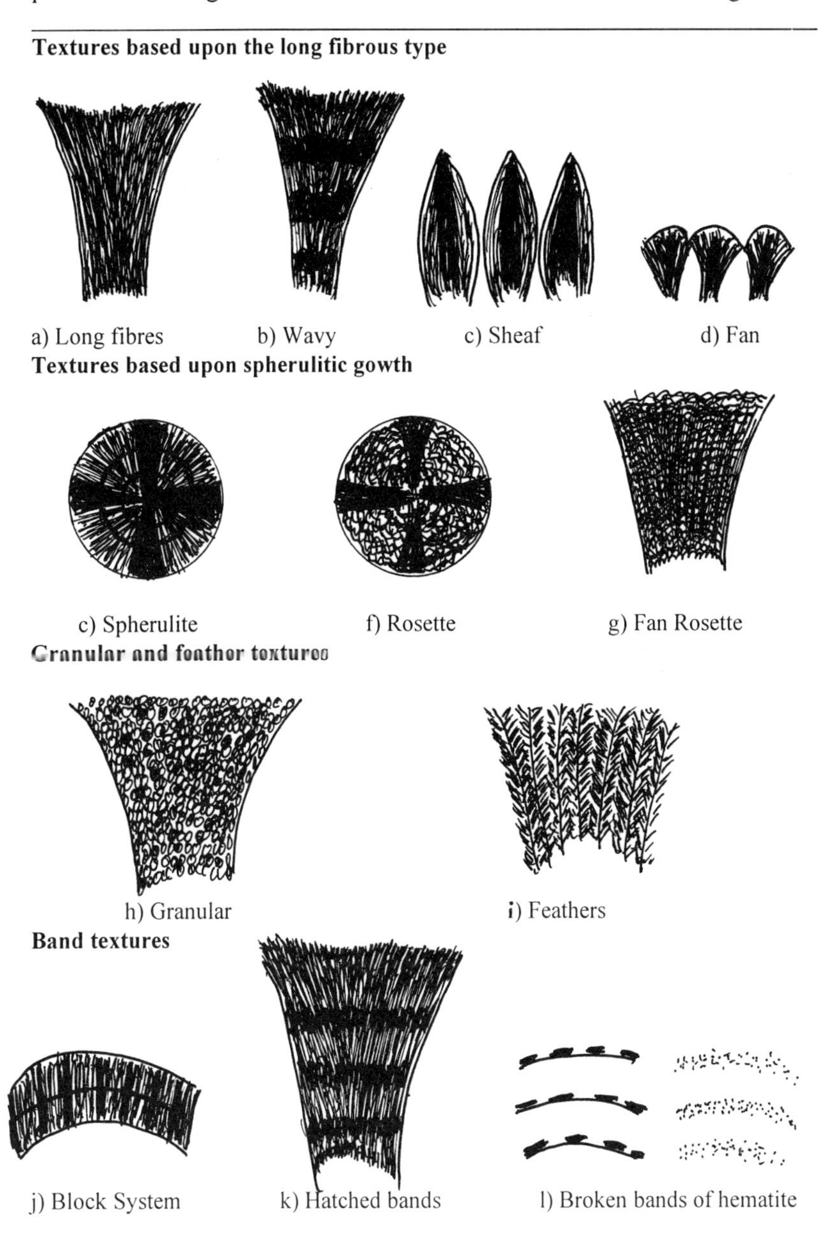

i) Feathers.The feather texture has only been observed in some horizontal banded agates from Dunure. These structures grow vertical to the bands although on occasions it has a wavy texture and resembles tongues of fire.

Bands within agate

j) Block bands. The band consists of blocks of fibres arranged in rows but the blocks are sometimes multiple. These bands have always been found in the outer layers.

k) Hatched bands. A light brown hatched band is revealed in transmitted light. While this banding is limited to the white and blue-white bands, it has been found in agates from Brazil, Botswana and Scotland.

l) Hematite. Hematite is shown in small patches apparently deposited when there is a pause in the crystallisation process.

3.2 General features

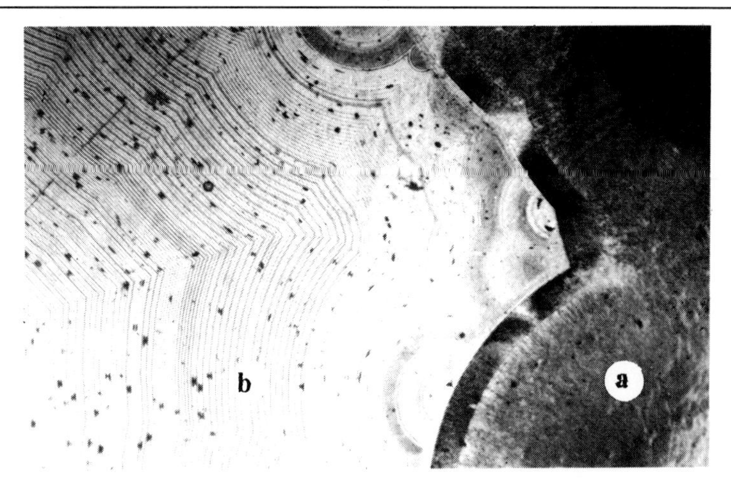

Fig. 3.3 The outer 2 mm (a) shows itself as a different morphology to the inner areas (b). Culzean, Ayrshire. Short edge represents 2 mm. (x 30, plane polarised light)

In spite of the unique textural form of each agate, there are sufficient features that are common to warrant discussion under this heading. Usually, the whole agate was not present on the slides and a comparison of the various structural types would be invalid. It would appear that a granular texture is common, occupying perhaps 10% of the total area in

fortification agate and 90% of the area in the horizontally banded type. The outer edge, approximately 1 to 2 mm in width, always reveals itself as having a distinctly different morphology to the inner area (Fig. 3.3). About a quarter of the author's collection of slides have a section of the outside edge and all but two were length fast. According to Folk and Pittman (1971), length slow **chalcedony** is evidence of deposition in an evaporitic or alkaline environment. They proposed that the silica deposited at low **pH** is highly polymerised. The silica chains lie tangentially to the growth giving a c axis at right angles to the fibres. However, the length slow chalcedony is formed from the silicate ions in an alkaline environment and the tetrahedral silica units align themselves with a c axis parallel to the fibres (Fig.3.4).The two, admittedly rare, length slow outer edges are apparent evidence for a distinct first generation of silica. Equally, it could be argued that this 'first generation' is really one of 'first crystallisation.'

Approximately 60% of the inner area is composed of typical chalcedonic quartz: the long fibrous growth type a. It frequently takes over from the sheaf-like forms type c and sweeps towards the centre.

Macroquartz is common with its presence being recorded on a number of slides and approximately 10% of the author's collection have macroquartz visible in the hand specimens. Quartz is usually found in the centre of the agate. The vast majority show a crystal growth that has been subject to an apparent temperature gradient: a fine saccharoidal first deposit grading to medium crystals and with the largest being found at the centre. Elongated quartz is always length slow and away from the initial growth an **undulatory extinction** is common. Clays and other foreign minerals are generally absent and lineage boundaries can only be observed with the polars crossed.

Footnote: *There are seven crystal systems and each system has reference axes known as crystallographic axes. By convention, the crystallographic axes are referred to as a,b and c. It is possible, using accessory plates, to find the orientation of the optic axis. If the c axis is perpendicular to the quartz fibres then the chalcedony is length fast. Conversely, when the c axis is parallel to the fibres it is length slow.*

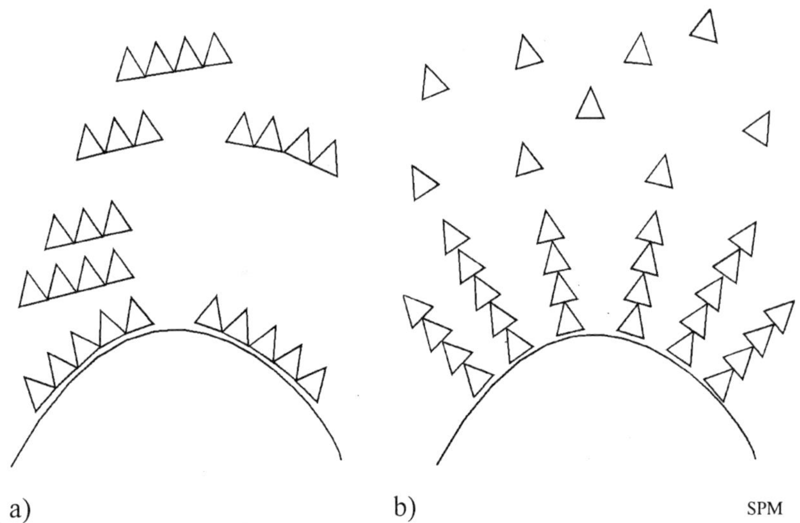

Fig. 3.4 a) In an acidic environment the silica tetrahedra are polymerised and attach themselves tangentially to the gel. The c axis lies parallel to the surface and at right angles to the direction of the fibres.

b) In an alkaline environment the silica can exist as monomers and these units attach themselves to the growing fibres on-by-one. After Folk and Pittman, 1971.

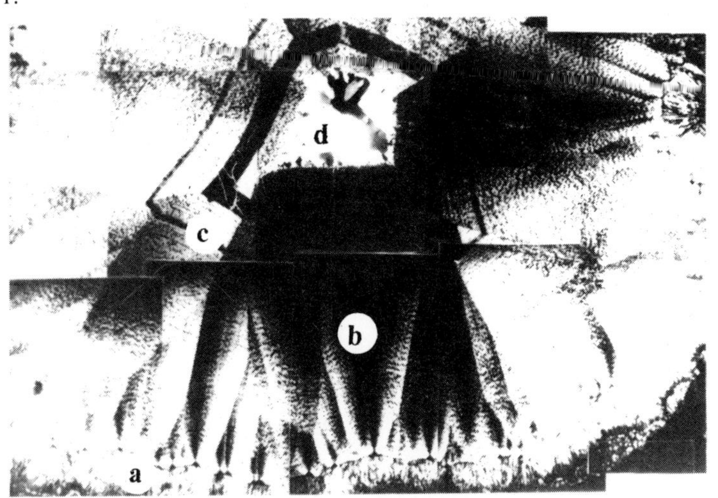

Fig.3.5 A composite micrograph shows the apparent 'first generation' of chalcedony (a). The 'second generation' of chalcedony (b) sweeps towards the centre. Spots of hematite are on the boundary line. Hematite bands are at (c) followed by quartz (d). Montrose, Angus. Short edge represents 2 cm. (x 3, crossed polars).

Frequently, the first quartz growth shows a transitional state between chalcedony and quartz: it retains the fibrous nature of the chalcedony but it is length slow and the quartz wedge shows that it is part of the quartz crystal. Occasionally, the crossed polars reveal a feathery smear within the quartz grains but as this effect is generally found in the early stages of growth it is assumed to be a strain effect within the crystals. Apart from the crystal size, there is little evidence of the growth of the grains; however some quartz does show zonal growth (Fig. 3.6). The nature of the zoning shows some contrast with the principles of geometrical selection applied to the growth of drusy quartz crystals (Grigorev, 1965).

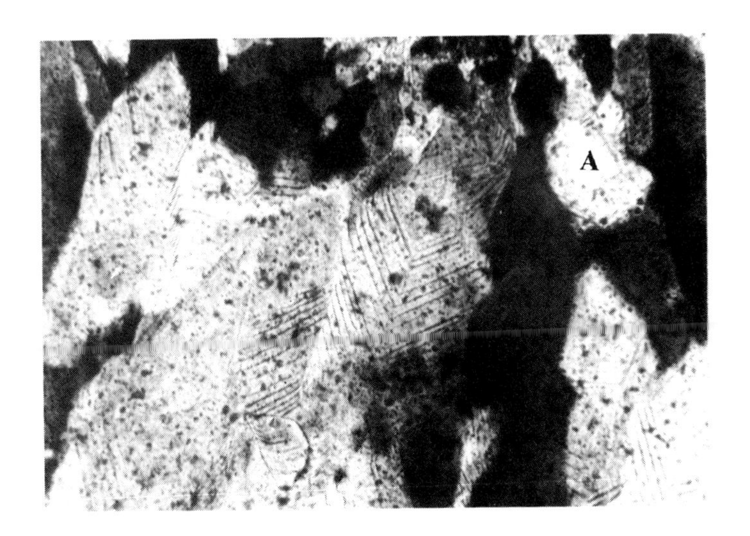

Fig. 3.6 Zoning is present in these quartz grains. The quartz grain (A) appears to have nucleated and grown with the silica having free access around the seeds. Maidens beach, Ayrshire.Short edge represents 2 mm. (x 30,crossed polars).

According to Grigorev (Fig. 3.7), there are three stages of common growth. The number of crystal individuals (P) as a percentage of total initiations is plotted against the distance from the surface of initial growth (S). The first stage shows many crystallites have the freedom to grow as separate entities until they meet other crystallites shown by segment a-b.

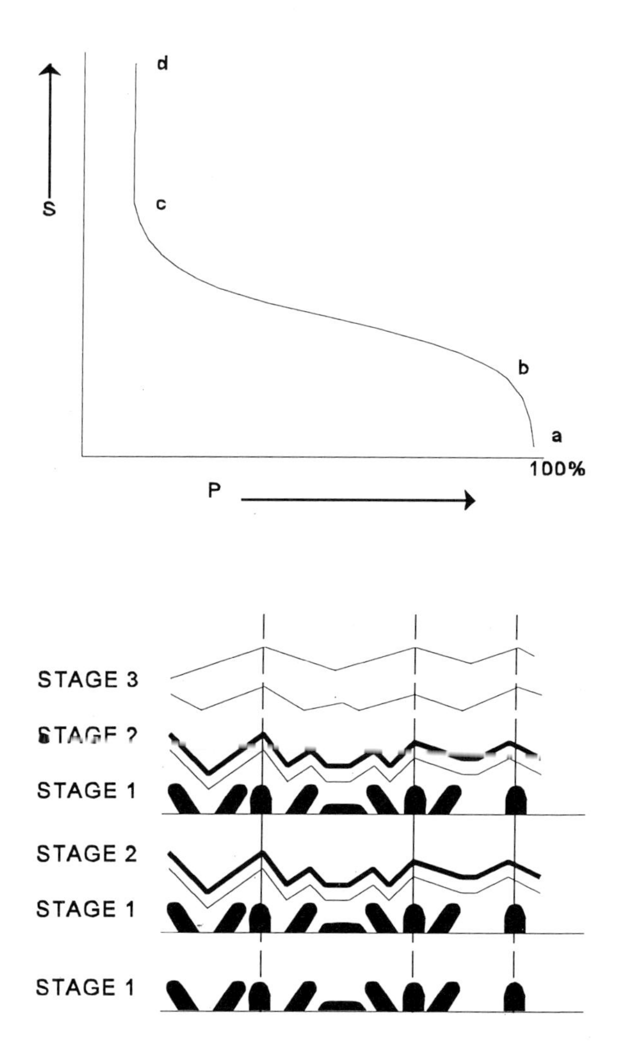

CdF

Fig. 3.7 The growth of drusy quartz crystals (after Grigorev, 1965)
P is the number of growing individuals expressed as a percentage of the total initiated.
S is the distance from the surface of the growth.
Stage 1 (and a-b) represents the growth of separate crystals.
Stage 2 (and b-c) represents druse growth and geometrical selection.
Stage 3 (and c-d) represents parallel-columnar growth.

When the crystals meet, geometrical selection occurs with the crystals having the most favourable orientation for growth surviving, shown by b-c. Stage three of druse growth is reached when parallel crystals are formed and theoretically the growth would continue infinitely (c-d) with no competition for space.

Agate 81 (Fig. 3.6) has zoned quartz crystals and stage one corresponds to that as outlined by Grigorev. During stage two, sufficient crystals nucleated and grew to a size before resting on the first formed crystals; subsequent growth is equal in all directions except where they meet other crystallites. Eventually, when they fill the space, growth continues towards the centre that then follows Grigorev's principle of geometrical selection. Petrographic observations in the non zoned quartz generally correspond with the zoned samples. Often, the area is much larger and they can fill the central portion with large individual crystals. The overall picture is of crystallisation from a sealed environment.

Fig. 3.8 is a composite photograph of agate in thin section. An outer rim (a) is clearly showing a contrasting morphology with the inner area as it gives way to a 'second generation' of **chalcedony** (b). This new growth sweeps towards the centre in the direction of the arrows. Eventually the iron oxide is precipitated (c) and this now rhythmically deposits with clear chalcedony. These deposits initially repeat the curves (Fig.3.3) in the rhythmic banding but as the centre is approached then Grigorev's principal of geometrical selection applies and many curved bands are lost. This smoothing of the bands is apparent if the final band at the centre is compared with the first iron oxide deposit at (b). Here, there is a final deposit of quartz crystals (d).

3.3 Petrographic examination of atypical agate samples

The general features that have been described in the last example (section 3.2) are to be observed in many agates. However, a few agates produce features that are unique or very rare.

Agate 148 (Fig. 3.9), pillar agate, was given to the author more than twenty years ago but it was only sliced recently. The delay was due to the question of my skills as a slide-maker and an awareness that the direction of slicing was irreversible. In the event, it was possible to produce a longitudinal and a transverse cross section as shown in Figs. 3.10 and 3.11.

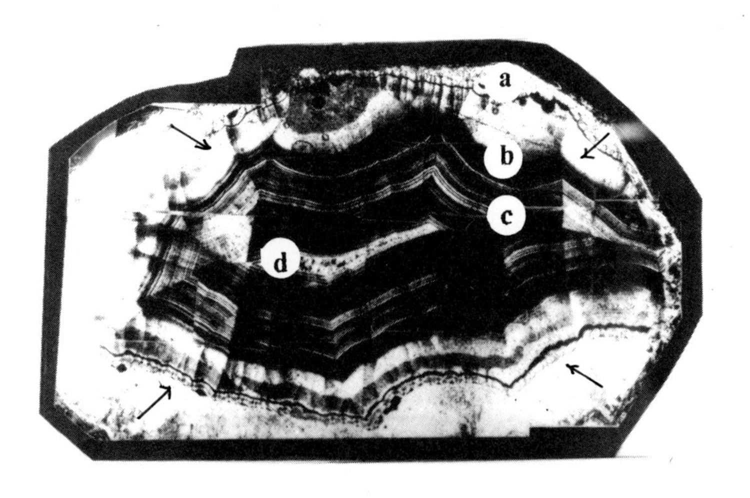

Fig. 3.8 Crystallisation starts from the outer edge (a) and sweeps towards the centre (b) depositing bands of hematite (c) and finishing with a quartz centre (d). Maidens beach. Short edge represents 2.5 cm. (x 2.4, crossed polars).

There has been much discussion over the last fifty years (chapter 7) regarding the form of silica that enters the vesicle: gel or solution. If the silica is transported as a solution, then pillar agates such as example 148 should grow as limestone stalactites and stalagmites. An examination of cross sections could produce evidence of distinct, separate growth. Conversely, if the agate precursor was a silica gel then the growth would be a single stage. Microscopic examination provides enough evidence to show that the growth of this agate was due to a single deposit and not a repeated deposition.

i) At first examination, Fig. 3.11 shows an apparent ring structure that could be due to multiple deposits of silica. However, the whole inner area between a and b contains spots of iron oxide and similar spots have been deposited within the outer wall area: e to d.

ii) Both the cross section of the outer wall (e to d) and the cross section of the touching pillar (c to a) show the same three distinct crystallisation morphologies. The wall has crystallised in the direction of the arrows while the pillar has crystallised from the centre outwards. The direction of crystallisation is confirmed by the middle band at d, b and a where the sheaf structure points outwards: from the centre of the pillar to the outer edge and from the outer to inner wall of the side wall.

iii) Fig. 3.10 shows the tapering of the pillar from roof to base; gravity would cause a thick hanging gel to thin at the base.

iv) The same three types of crystallisation morphology are shown in both Fig. 3.10 and 3.11 except that the outer crystallisation is lost at the base of the pillar (Fig. 3.10).

This distinctive agate-type does not contradict the earlier statement that crystallisation is a single step process.

The block of Burn Anne agate (Fig. 3.12) typifies the problems posed by any attempts to explain agate genesis. Both the lava and agate would be penecontemporaneous: the agate adopts the rough outline of the lava and yet it encapsulates lava fragments. In addition, the lava has surrounded a red agate fraction that is clearly part of the red **fortification** pattern.

Agate 24 is a toffee brown, red brown and white agate from Maidens, Ayrshire. The outer edge is red brown and under the microscope the fine, opaque, red, hematite spots are revealed. The inner area contains larger spots of hematatite and the texture is almost granular. However, at the centre yellow oily globules (~ 100μm) with clinging hematite balls (~ 20μm) can be observed. This is the only agate where I have observed both hematite (red) and what is presumed goethite (yellow) co-existing in the same globular form (Fig. 3.13).

Fig. 3.9 After lying in my garage for a number of years, this fractured pillar agate (No 148) has become a home for spiders. Actual size.

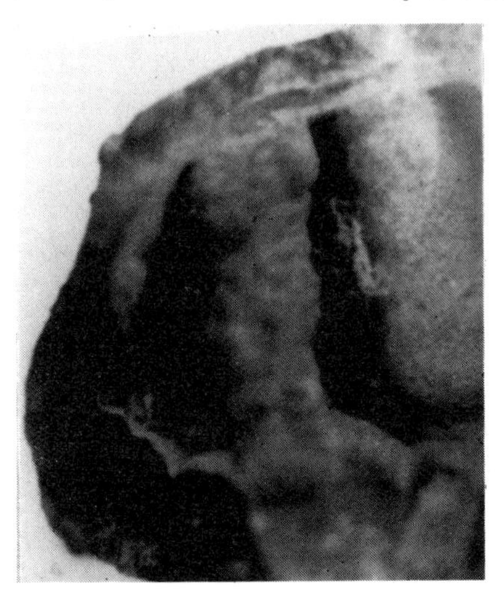

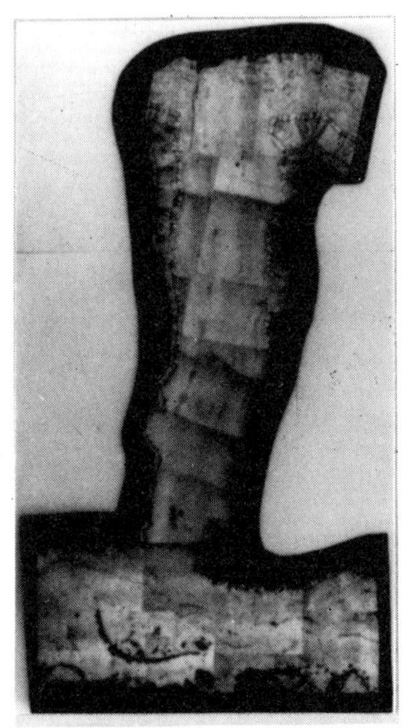

Fig. 3.10 Longitudinal cross section of a pillar in agate (148). Composite micrograph, x 1.5, polars crossed. Long edge represents 5.3 cm

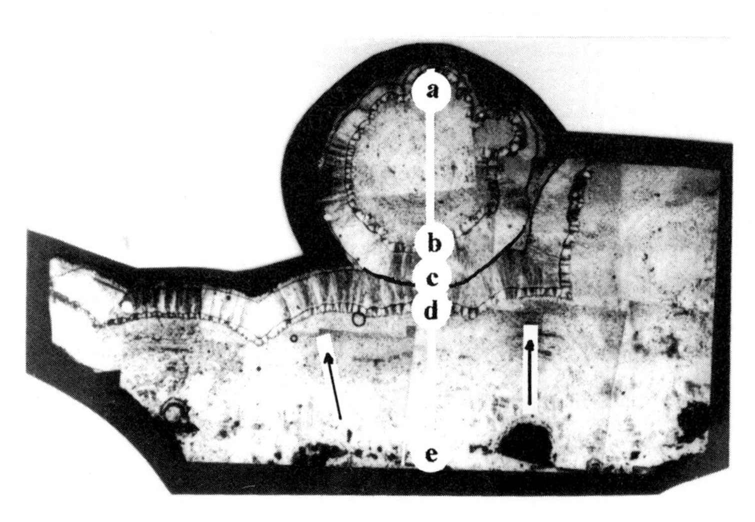

Fig. 3.11 Transverse cross section of a pillar in agate 148. Composite micrograph, x 2, polars crossed. Short edge represents 3 cm.

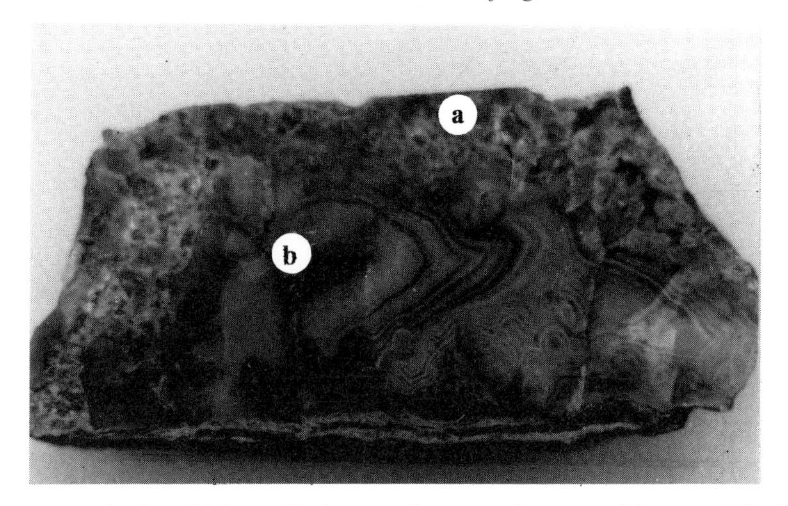

Fig. 3.12 The lava (a) has split the agate but agate fragments (b) are contained within the lava. Burn Anne. Actual size.

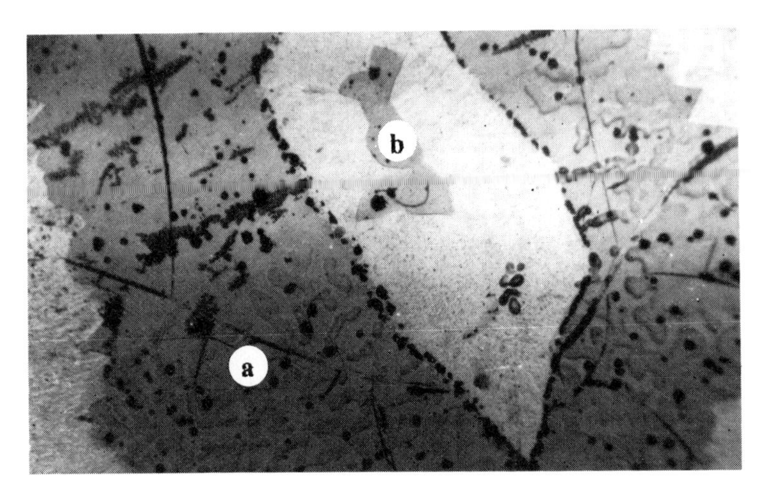

Fig. 3.13 The crystallisation front has pushed small yellow globules and clinging spots of red hematite towards the centre . The globules have all deposited within this area (a). A globule-free area continues until the remaining spots are deposited at (b). The area containing the globules is light brown. Agate 24, Maidens beach, Ayrshire. Short edge represents 4 mm. (x 15, plane polarised light).

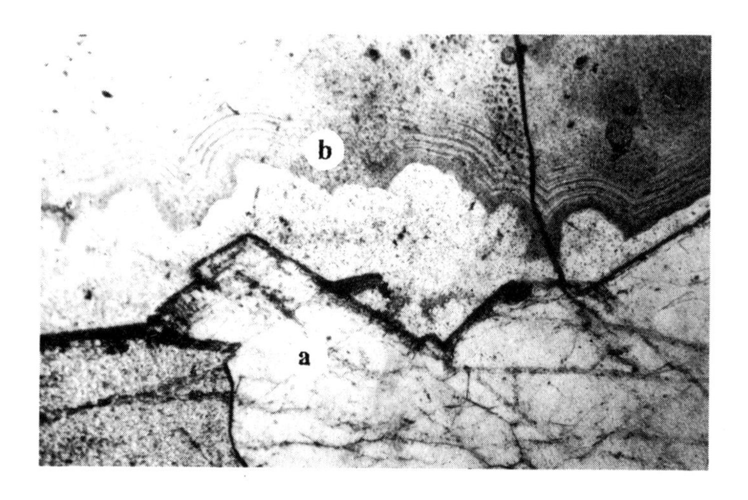

Fig. 3.14 Calcite (a) and chalcedony (b) in contact. Agate 57, Maidens, Ayrshire. Short edge represents 2 mm. (x 30, plane polarised light).

3.4 Iris agate

Iris agate or iridescent agate shows spectral colours when viewed in transmitted light. The ability of agate to act as a diffraction grating has been known since the last century and the reason is popularly thought to be due to the fineness of the bands. However, according to Jones (1951), the bands in iris agate can range from 4 000 down to a few hundred lines /cm and the grating structure is due to alternate layers having higher and lower **refractive indices**.

The iridescence is best observed when a thin section slide is slowly rotated in the path of strong light. Four samples have been found; each from separate regions of the Midland Valley. This would confirm the observation made by Jones that iris agate is a peculiarity of the crystallisation process and as such could be found in any agate-bearing locality. The bands in these Midland Valley samples had a frequency from 1 000 to 4 000 /cm and were generally in a band width of about 0.05 mm.

3.5 Associated Minerals

In the past, many associated minerals have been reportedly found with agate. Smith (1910) lists a variety of minerals that include very rare occurrences of pyrites and galena but the majority would now be regarded as forms of silica. **Chlorite**, calcite and **celadonite** are the common exceptions.

Fig. 3.14 shows a typical calcite/ chalcedony contact, in that the chalcedony appears to have entered the vesicle at a later stage and crystallised on the rhombohedral calcite. While there is little evidence of acid erosion and then replacement, there is always an indistinct penetration of the calcite.

3.6 Agate under the electron microscope

The transmission electron microscope is comparable to the transmission optical light microscope except that **electrons** are used instead of light. Electrons react strongly with all matter and any examination of material can only be carried out if the original section is exceptionally thin or by using a replica technique. In this investigation, a freshly fractured unpolished surface of agate was coated with polyvinyl alcohol. After hardening, the dried alcohol strip was removed from the surface of the agate and a negative image was obtained. Sections were cut and shadowed with platinum and carbon. The polyvinyl alcohol was dissolved in water and the platinum carbon shadow floated onto copper grids for examination under the TEM.

A scanning electron microscope (SEM) is analogous to the reflecting light microscope: an electron beam is aimed at the surface of the material shadowed with gold or carbon. The surface can be freshly fractured or polished. During this study both types of agate surfaces have been examined.

Electron microscope examination of fine grained silica minerals is fairly limited in literature. However, sufficient work was done to confirm the first electron microscope observations on chert by Folk and Weaver in 1952, who recognised two end members of the surface morphology as 'spongy' and 'novaculite' (*an American term used to describe certain **Precambrian cherts***). The spongy texture is described as,

> like a piece of Swiss cheese, while the novaculite type appears as a series of quartz crystal blocks locked together as in the manner of crazy paving.

A third textural surface is described as intermediate between the two end members and has a surface with far fewer cavities and indistinct grains. Further electron microscope studies on chert by Pittman(1959) and Oldershaw (1968) have confirmed the surface texture described by Folk and Weaver. Similar studies on agate are few but Kaibara (1964) and Monroe (1964) using the TEM agreed with Folk and Weaver. Sunagawa and Ohta (1976) were the first to report evidence of the **petrographic fibrosity** with the TEM. However Lange et al. (1984), using the SEM, described the surface as consisting of small globulites but were unable to find any fibrosity.

For this investigation, white or blue white bands in agate when viewed under the optical microscope, always showed a marked contrast in texture when compared with the non banded regions within the same agate. Agate 10 was purchased as Botswana fortification agate and in thin section the white bands reveal an acicular (*hatched texture*) while the clear chalcedony shows a coarse fibrous texture (Fig 3.15). The comparable morphology under the TEM is shown in Fig. 3.16. Quartz grains up to 2 **μm** are found in the clear chalcedony while the white bands are flat and have distinct parallel breaks. The SEM shows that the flat areas consist of a ridged pimpled surface and Fig. 3.17 portrays a junction within the white band in agate 10 as it changes direction. As the surface in the TE micrograph (Fig. 3.18) is a negative and the surface shown in the SE micrograph (Fig. 3.17) is actual, then the dimples and valleys shown in the TE micrograph are the pimples and ridges in the SE micrograph. The texture of the white bands is plate-like and the acicular texture is the result of the end view of these plate-like growths.

The series of TE micrographs of agate taken in this study are in conflict with the description of chalcedonic chert provided by Folk and Weaver (1952): the clear chalcedony in this set of micrographs of chalcedonic agate shows evidence of fibrosity that is in contrast with the microtexture of chert. Furthermore, neither the neat equant interlocking quartz grains nor the spongy surfaces observed by Folk and Weaver have been observed in any of these TEM agate micrographs. It has been suggested that the flat areas in the non banded regions correspond to the optical **fibrosity** and such differences between chalcedonic chert and agate are the result of the environment and method of deposition (Moxon, 1991).

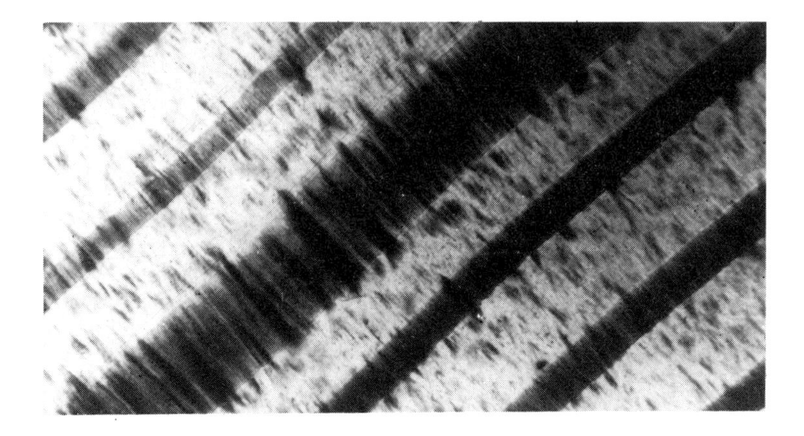

Fig 3.15 Optical micrograph of agate 10 showing the stacked plate-like texture of the white bands. Short edge represents 0.9 mm.(x 60, crossed polars).

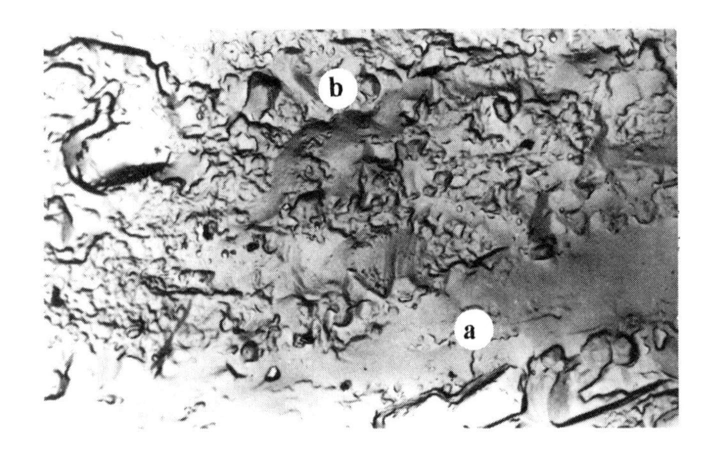

Fig. 3.16 TEM of clear chalcedony in a Tayport agate. The micrograph shows fibrosity (a) and granular regions (b). Short edge represents 6 μm. (x 9 000).

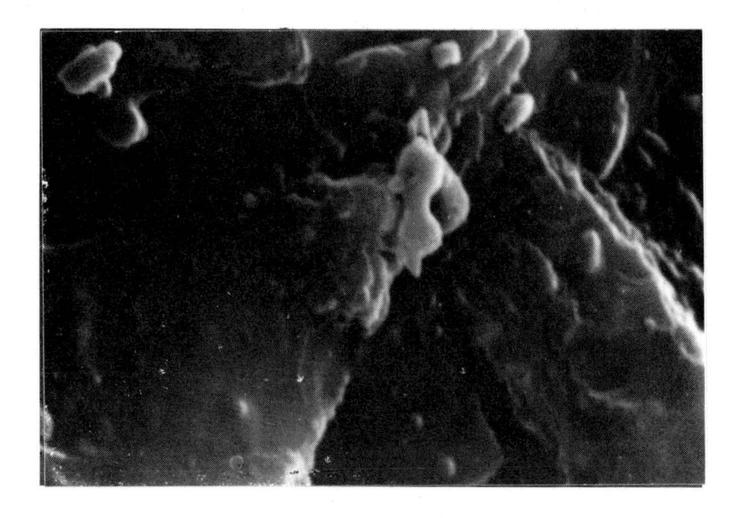

Fig 3.17 SEM of agate with the central line showing a junction as the white band changes direction. Short edge represents 15 μm. (x 4 000).

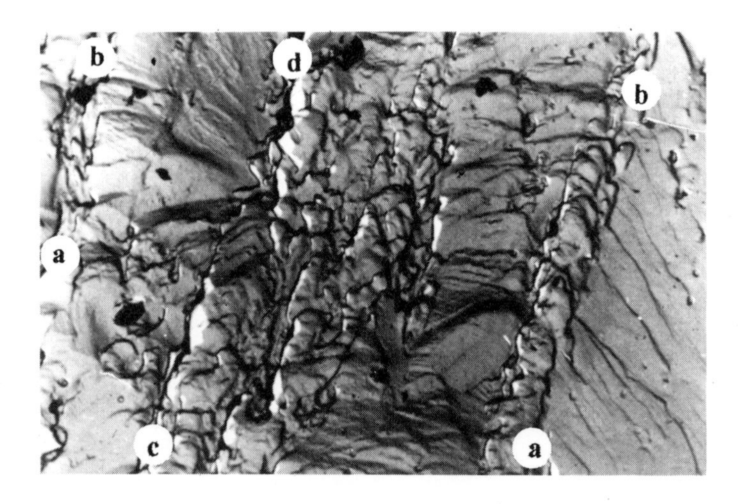

Fig. 3.18 TEM of the white band in agate 10. a to b and c to d show the junction between the edges of the stacked plates. Short edge represents 6 μm. (x 10 000).

Chapter 4 Colour in agate

The demands of the jewellery trade for natural and synthetic quartz has prompted much research into the cause of colour in crystalline silica. Pure quartz is colourless and trace metal **ions** are responsible for the major coloured quartz minerals of amethyst (purple), citrine (yellow) and smoky quartz (brown). Ionising radiation also plays an important role in creating colour within the coloured varieties of quartz. However, the actual cause of the colouration in agate has not attracted much attention in the scientific literature: any comments are usually limited to suggestions of trace metal ions or optical effects.

4.1 The brown colour shown by some agate bands in transmitted light.

Many minerals produce a change in colour when examined in transmitted light. Agate is no exception and translucent white, blue, purple, black and purple red are brown when viewed in transmitted light. The phenomenon is most strong with the blue-white and white bands and the brown colour remains at standard **thin section** thickness of 0.03 mm. Reis (1917) described white bands that are cloudy oil yellow when viewed under these conditions. In recent times, this brown colour has been observed in certain **cherts** and was discussed in detail by Pelto (1956).

Pelto investigated the brown colour of some varieties of **chalcedony** in transmitted light. According to him,

> the brown colour is found only rarely or faintly in agate but is strong in many cherts and chalcedony. When found, it can usually be shown to follow the Tyndall effect: the scattering of light.

Rayleigh's scattering formula relates the intensity of scattered light to the intensity of incident light. An abbreviated version of the formula is:

$$I_s \propto I \cdot \frac{1}{\lambda^4}$$

Is = intensity of scattered light
I = intensity of incident light
λ = wavelength of light

Large bubbles would scatter light without altering its colour. As the size of the particles becomes smaller than the wavelength of light, then the scatter effect is greatest with the smallest end of the spectrum: blue light. The general effect is that the greatest scatter would be found with small **inclusions** and the major loss of light is at the blue end of the spectrum: the transmitted light would be red-brown.

Dodge (1948) described a technique to find the refractive index of mineral grains using a dark field oil immersion method. The same procedure can be used to produce the scattering effect provided a good blue light transmission is obtained. These conditions can be achieved if an oil is used that has a refractive index equal or less than the least index of the particles. For agate grains, clove oil has the correct refractive index of 1.535 at 20°C and produces violet, blue and orange to red colours at the junction of liquid and particle edge.

The amateur microscopist can easily obtain dark field illumination at home. In essence, these conditions are achieved when a hollow cone of light is greater than the angular aperture of the objective lens. Without material on the microscope stage, the light misses the objective and the field of view is dark. Crystal grains can reflect and refract light and they appear luminous against a dark background. The necessary dark field conditions can be achieved by sticking a circular opaque stop on a transparent plastic disc and fitting the disc in the filter carrier. Moxon (1991) described the use of the technique to examine agate grains. Black and dark purple coloured bands from agate were shown to contain tiny illuminated holes. Colourless samples of chalcedony from the same agates contained far fewer holes or were entirely free from these **inclusions**. In both cases, pores occupied up to 50% of the total area and the scattering effect was the same in the black and dark purple bands. It would appear that the most likely cause of the dark purple and black colours is the ability of inclusions to scatter nearly all, or totally, incident light. However, the same series of experiments showed that the light scattering ability was greatest with the translucent white and blue-white bands (Fig. 4.1). The SEM and TEM in Figs. 3.17, 3.18 show that the bands consist of a series of stacked plate-like structures. The plate edges at around 2-10 μm are small enough to affect light. Any light that is bounced off the edge of the plates would result in the blue component being most easily scattered. Thicker slices would be expected to scatter more of the transmitted blue component of light. This would produce a darker red colour as more of the blue light fraction is lost; this is observed in practice.

Fig. 4.1The large grain consists of alternating blue-white and clear bands. Blue-white bands (illuminated) consist of the plate-like structure and these bands can scatter light. Clear bands are dark. Top edge represents 0.9mm.(x 60, dark field illumination).

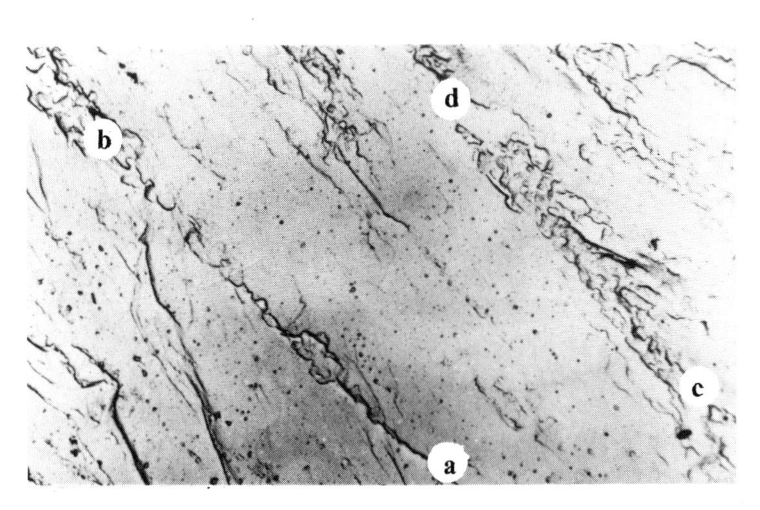

Fig. 4.2 Dusty inclusions are responsible for scattering reflected white light and this scatter means that the bands appear blue-white. Lines a to b and c to d show divisions between the plates. Short edge represents 24 μm. (x 2 500).

4.2 Colour in blue-white bands

Agate 71 is a **fortification** agate with blue-white bands alternating with clear chalcedony and in thin section the blue-white bands produce an acicular *(hatched)* texture that is indistinguishable from translucent white bands in other agates eg agate 10 (Fig. 3.15). However, the TE micrograph of the blue-white bands also contains dusty inclusions within the plate structure (Fig. 4.2). These bubbles are approximately 0.02 μm in diameter and have a bubble density of ~ 30 $/\mu m^2$. However, the bubbles are of a different type and are far from showing the coalescence as described by Folk and Weaver (1952). These dusty **inclusions** are responsible for the blue-white colour as they will scatter incident light in a similar manner to cigarette smoke particles (*Tyndall effect*).

4.3 Translucent red and yellow

Any collector of Scottish agate has to work very hard to build up a representative collection. However, there is much pleasure when samples are found as the quality is superb. This is always noticeable when Scottish agate is compared with the slabs of Brazilian agate that can be found in many dealers' cabinets. These blue and green polished specimens look what they are: artificially dyed. Each collector of Scottish agate will have particular favourites: perhaps the inky blue and white agates from the Blue Hole at Usan or the delicate blue grey and orange from Ballindean. However, all who have seen the rich red and yellow agates of Burn Anne must regard them highly. Macpherson (1989) mentions reported early workings that occurred on both banks of Burn Anne. If they did exist, they have long gone and finding agate in or around the Burn is very difficult for the casual visitor. I am indebted to John Raeburn who has allowed me to have samples of this magnificent agate from his personal collection.The following descriptions show some varieties that have been recovered from the Burn.

Agate 11094 is a piece of jasper agate measuring ~ 50 x 60 x 10 mm . The pattern is a complex mixture of red, orange and yellow with small patches of blue-grey and clear fortification pattern. Some central areas are full of microquartz crystals. The agate when wet has the element of translucency that always distinguishes agate from the dull appearance of the clay, yellow and red iron oxide that is found in jasper. In thin section, the specimen is full of surprises. Normally, the yellow colours in the Burn Anne agate are due to small oily looking globules of goethite. In this sample, the yellow areas have developed because of dendritic growth and the red **hematite** remains opaque at the standard 0.03 mm. However, the orange colour has formed a series of hair-like intergrowths, finer but reminiscent of rutilated quartz; this type of growth in agate is unique in this author's experience (Fig. 4.3). Most of the microstructure is granular with evidence of fibrous chalcedony mainly limited to the blue-grey banding.

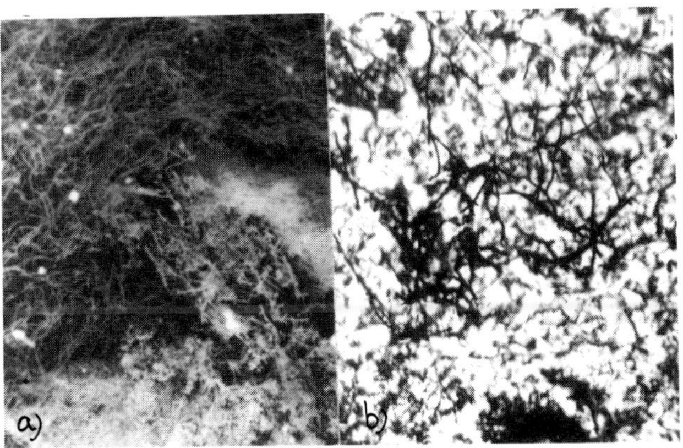

Fig. 4.3 Hair-like growths in a sample of Burn Anne agate. a) Reflected light x 30 b) Transmitted light x 50. Short edge represents 1.8 and 1.1 mm respectively.

A typical Burn Anne agate contains yellow oily globules and red hematite spots. In thin section, the yellow colour is observed as semi-translucent yellow and may be an alteration product of the red hematite. Fig. 4.4 shows a transition between the two colours as the red band gives way to a more diffuse series of yellow spots. The yellow spots have been analysed using the Energy Dispersive X-ray analysis system and the spots are shown to containing a variable amount of iron (analysed as Fe_2O_3). Concentration of iron oxide is about three times greater in the rim than the central region. This would suggest that iron oxide diffusion has had time to occur before crystallisation had taken place (Fig. 4.5).

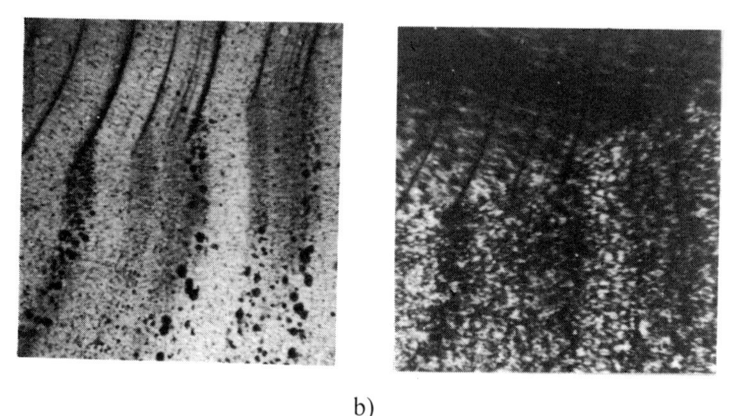

a) b)
Fig. 4.4 A transition between yellow spots (lower) and red bands (upper). Burn Anne agate, x 40. a) plane polarised light. b) crossed polars.Top edge represents 1.1 mm.

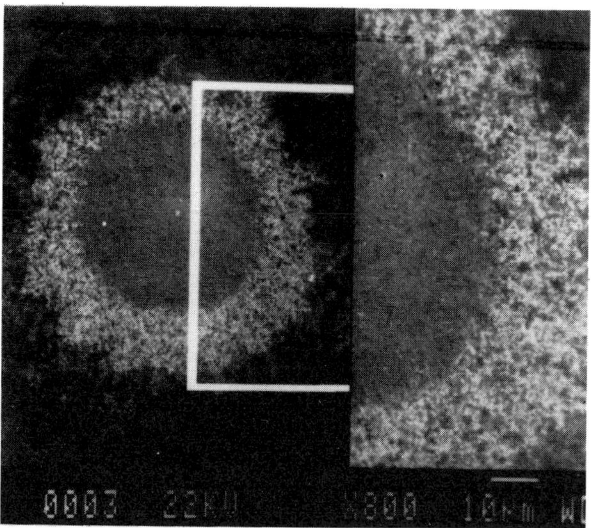

Fig. 4.5 The yellow globules produce this halo effect. The change in concentration is indicative of a diffusion mechanism. SEM x 800.

Heddle (1901) described the jasper vein agate of Burn Anne as brick shaped segments cemented by magnesium dolomite. He suggested that the coagulating silica filled the rectangular spaces and further fracturing resulted in the brick-shaped agates being cemented by a subsequent secondary filling of dolomitic paste. However, the red brick-shaped samples that I have examined were cemented by secondary **microquartz**.

4.4 Opaque colours

Many agates contain an opaque white colour that, until the work of Midgley (1951), was thought to be due to an increased **opal** content. For the first half of the twentieth century, chalcedony was regarded as a mixture of opal and quartz although it had long been known that chalcedony always gave a quartz X-ray diffraction pattern. Midgley with Folk and Weaver (1952) were independently able to show that the structure of chalcedony could be explained in terms of a quartz with holes theory; this provided an adequate explanation for any anomalous properties shown by chalcedony. The opaque white bands are particularly noticeable in horizontally banded agate and in thin section such bands are cloudy but fibrous chalcedony can be observed.

Opaque colours found in the Midland Valley are typically shades of red and brown which grade into a yellow colour. If these colours cannot be observed as an opaque material in thin section, then it would appear that trace impurity can be responsible for quite intense colouration. Fig 4.6 is a cross section of a cylindrical agate with rings of various shades of brown and white. The bands have been examined under the SEM and the darkest brown band did show approximately more Fe^{3+} (0.5%) than the lighter bands (0.2%) and, as is frequently observed, the iron compounds have altered the surface morphology. This type of agate colouration is particularly problematical and would profit from more detailed analysis.

Fig. 4.6 The different colours show different textures and the dark brown bands have the greater concentration of iron oxide. Actual size.

Chapter 5 Rhythmic banding in simulation experiments

Fig. 5.1 Orbicular diorite. Courtesy Dept. Earth Sciences, Cambridge University.

Rhythmic banding in agate is just one example of repetitive formations that can be observed in nature. Moulds and annular rings in trees are clear examples where ring structures are added to existing formations through further growth; in other cases, the pattern develops within an already defined medium eg orbicular diorite (Fig. 5.1). However, the manner of the formation of agate banding is not obvious. One of the earliest simulation experiments that attempted to link the observed banding to agate genesis was carried out by the French experimental mineralogist Daubrée, who in 1880, subjected bottle glass to a high temperature **hydrothermal** attack. Similar experiments were carried out by Nacken (1948) and White and Corwin (1961); although it was Liesegang's 1896 experiments with gels that lead, in 1915, to the simulation of most agate types.

5.1 Liesegang Rings.

Fig. 5.2 Iron silicate growths produced from iron (II) sulphate in sodium silicate.

Raphael Liesegang (1869-1947) was an outstanding colloid chemist whose scientific interests included early developments in photography, bacteriology, origins of silicosis and the study of crystal growth in gels. Periodic ring formation in a variety of organic and inorganic compounds had been known since 1850. By 1913, Liesegang's contributions resulted in the phenomenon being known as the 'Liesegang Rings.' Scientific interest in rhythmic banding has continued and hardly any rhythmic pattern has escaped a possible link with Liesegang Rings: solidification of melted aspirin, patterns on butterfly wings, synthetic mother- of- pearl are just three of the diverse topics involving rhythmic banding to be studied. By 1965, more than 800 scientific papers had been published on this phenomenon.

Liesegang wrote over thirty papers on rhythmic precipitation, although it is his contributions on agate genesis that are the best known. The present day popular supplement to children's Chemistry Kits, 'The Chemical Garden', was used by Liesegang to suggest a mechanism for the formation of moss agate. When coloured metal compounds are added to a concentrated solution of sodium silicate (water glass) the outer layer of metal ion dissolves and forms the metal silicate. This silicate acts as a semi-permeable membrane; **osmosis** creates sufficient pressure for the membrane to burst and new metal **ions** are exposed to fresh silicate solution. Density differences allow the thread-like growths to rise. If iron (II) (*ferrous*) sulphate is used, then the resulting pattern is very similar to moss agate (Fig. 5.2).

Horizontally banded agate (German: Uruguay-Bänderung) is the second major agate type and in many ways the banded gel produces the most superficial likeness between a simulated pattern and genuine agate. Liesegang's original experiment described a layer of concentrated hydrochloric acid on a **silica gel** producing a white rhythmic deposit of silica. If the banded gel is now surrounded by a 20% solution of iron (III) (*ferric*) chloride, then the Fe^{3+} works its way between the silica and gives an imitation of horizontally banded agate. Several hypotheses have been proposed in an attempt to explain the banding phenomenon. Stern (1954) believed that Ostwald's (1897) original supersaturation theory was adequate. Adsorption of **ions** plays a part but the rhythmic banding occurs even with large crystals over long distances leaving diffusion as the major mechanism.

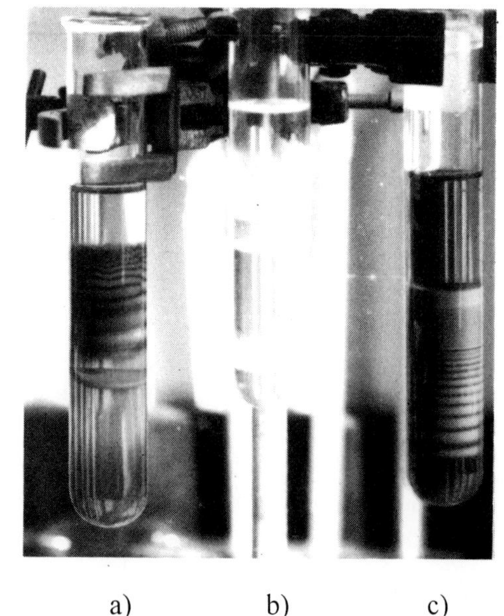

Fig. 5.3 Rhythmic banding in silica gel.

a) copper chromate

b) magnesium hydroxide

c) silver chromate.

Many media can allow the production of rhythmic banding and air plays this role in the reaction between the gases ammonia and hydrogen chloride. Under normal circumstances, the mixing of these gases produces a white smoke of solid ammonium chloride. However, if two cotton wool plugs soaked in concentrated hydrochloric acid and ammonium hydroxide are placed at either end of a long glass tube, then the diffusing ammonia and hydrogen chloride meet and produce a single white ring near to the heavier hydrochloric acid end. Single rings continue to be formed although the solid ammonium chloride does tend to sink to the bottom of the tube.

Nacken (1948) and Schlossmacher (1950) used earlier experiments involving crystallisation from a silica glass as a model for agate genesis that was based upon immiscible melt droplets. Rhythmic banding is often produced from melts and is readily obtained from liquid sulphur. When sulphur is gently heated, it melts at 113°C forming an amber melt of sulphur. If the liquid is rapidly poured out of the tube, the thin film remaining allows rhythmic banding to develop from the residual melt (Figs. 5.4,5.5). Any attempt at reproduction of the sulphur experiments will often be frustrated because of differences in the heating rate and the subsequent behaviour of the S_8 molecules. The initial heating results in the collapse of the sulphur crystal structure and the S_8 rings enter the molten state. Further heating allows some S_8 rings to break open and link with others to form very long sulphur chains. Some chains will break open and form simpler sulphur molecules of the S_2, S_4 or S_6 type. In essence, the melt will be a variable mixture that allows the formation of a regular rhythmic banding (Fig. 5.4) or spherulitic growth (Fig. 5.5). Both types of structures can be observed in agate and the mechanism of crystallisation from a multi-component polymeric **sol** of silica has been used to argue agate genesis (Chapter 8).

The author thought that these observations on the rhythmic banding from molten sulphur that he made in the mid 1970's were original; they had in fact been recorded in the scientific literature in 1915!

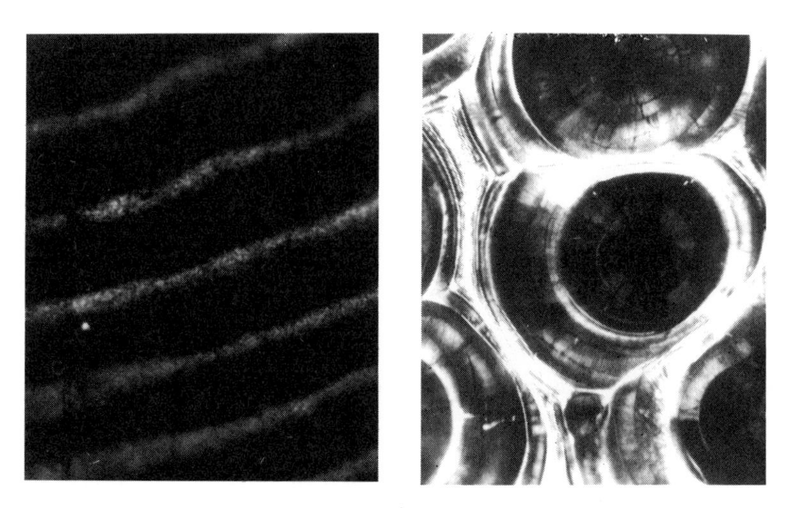

Fig. 5.4 Fig. 5.5

Fig. 5.4 Liesegang rhythmic banding produced when sulphur is rapidly poured out of a test tube (x 40, plane polarised light).

Fig. 5.5 On a separate occasion small spherulites are produced from the sulphur. Top edge represents 1.25 mm. (x 40, plane polarised light).

Fig. 5.6 Agate-type banding that has etched onto the back of a steel clock. Scale - hole diameter = 1 cm. Courtesy, J Raeburn.

One of the best examples of simulated agate pattern that the author has seen is shown in Fig. 5.6. The banding totally mimics a fortification agate but unfortunately the development of the pattern is the only part that could be linked to the story of agate genesis. The bands have formed on a steel plate that was originally a support backing for a quartz clock. The spindle that passed through the hole was brass and the backplate had clearly been handled as faint ghosts of finger prints can be observed. This selective etching was caused by the brass spindle in contact with the iron plate and together they behaved as electrodes for a simple electrolytic cell. If moisture and salt had been deposited during handling, then the surface of the iron would go into solution and the clock battery, although not essential for corrosion, may have been an added driving force in the etching process.

5.2 Mixing immiscible gels

Sodium silicate (sold under the trade name of water glass) is a thick syrupy, colourless liquid that behaves as a weak base when reacted with an acid:

$$Na_2SiO_3 + H_2O + 2HCl \longrightarrow Si(OH)_4 + 2\,NaCl$$

A supersaturated solution of silicic acid is formed and this unstable solution results in a condensation **polymerisation** reaction taking place. This actual polymerisation reaction is complex (the interested reader should consult Iler, 1979) but the final product at acid **pH** values is a three-dimensional gel. Silica particles at pH values >2 carry a negative charge and this allows the surface adsorption of positively charged cations or dyes. These particles act as a bridging effect of the silica that in turn would accelerate polymerisation. However, the dyes are sufficiently strongly adsorbed so that different dyed silica sols retain their separate colours when mixed. The overall effect is to produce a parallel banding in addition to rhythmic **fortification** patterns.

Similar effects can be achieved with polyester resins. When two differently coloured, liquid resins are mixed then diffusion occurs and the result is a single combined colour. If a thixotropic resin gel (silica base) is diluted with neat polyester resin, separately coloured and mixed, then the final product is a mixture of two immiscible coloured components. Many different effects can be obtained when coloured silicified resins are simultaneously poured into a mould.

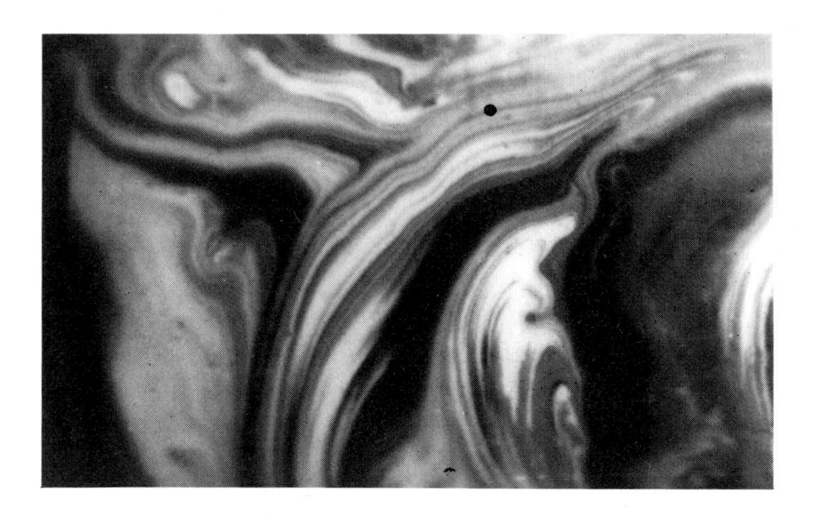

Fig. 5.7 Flow pattern produced when treated coloured resins are poured into a mould. Actual size.

Fig. 5.7 shows part of a 15 x 9 cm block of coloured polyester resin that has formed from a single pouring point of brown, orange and white silicified resin. The colours have not mixed and the natural flow and later interference are recorded in the cured block. A close-up of a black and white block is shown in Fig. 5.8 and here, the rising air bubbles have produced the fortification pattern at A and B. Unless great care is taken during the mixing process, air becomes trapped and the air bubbles slowly rise up through the gel. Many bubbles escape but a number are trapped and the pathway is revealed by the ripple effect when the block is sliced.

A direct comparison between these simulated fortification patterns and agate is not intended. However, there are examples where this mixing mechanism could account for complex agate patterns. The formation of some types of vein agate could be explained as a mixing of an iron-rich and an iron-poor **silica gel**. Once within the vein, the crystallisation could continue as explained in Chapter 8.

'Blow holes' are not a common pattern but they can be observed in a number of agates. These features appear as neat circles within the general texture of the agate. It has been suggested that their formation is due to air bubbles rising and creating holes in the gel; at a later date, a silica sol/ solution diffuses from the surrounding gel to crystallise in a different form (Moxon, 1996).

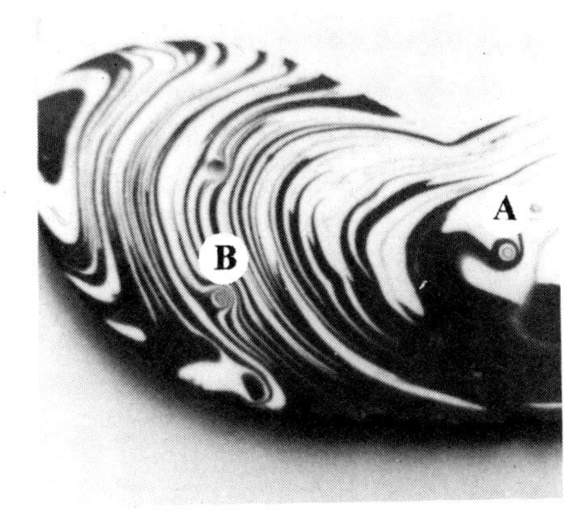

Fig. 5.8 A fortification pattern has been produced and rising air bubbles have caused the ripple effects at A and B. Actual size

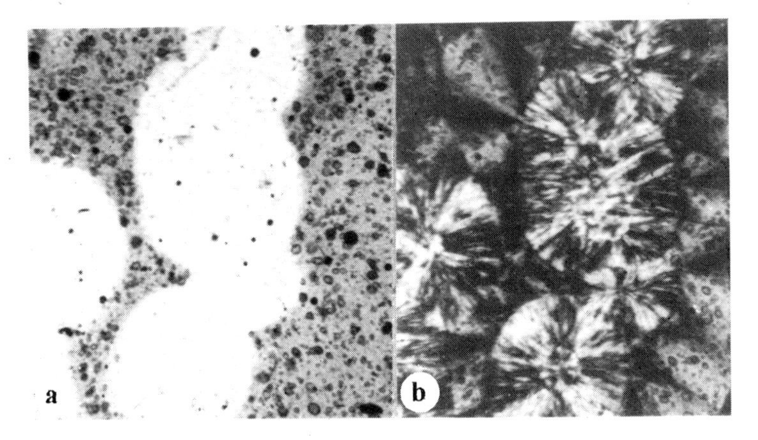

Fig. 5.9 a) 'Blow holes' in agate with the spherulites virtually free of iron oxide. Burn Anne agate, Kilmarnock. (x 40, plane polarised light).Scale = 0.5 mm. b) as a) with crossed polars. Side edge represents 1.3 mm.

Chapter 6 Crystallisation of silica from glass, gels, solution and the amorphous state

Many hypotheses of agate genesis have neglected to refer to the crystallisation of silica. Most of the published literature has either ignored the question or dismissed the process as a combination of time, pressure and temperature. The silica starting material is of prime importance and any discussion on agate genesis must account for the changes that occur between a proposed silica source and the fibrous quartz that is agate.

With field observations based on the Idaho fossil wood, Liesegang (1915) stated that the gel crystallised via **opal** into **chalcedony** or quartz, while Nacken (1948) cited his own experimental work for the crystallisation of glass into chalcedony.

This chapter discusses the experimental work done over the last forty years on the crystallisation of silica. Consideration of the various polymorphic forms of silica and their transition temperatures is only mentioned when they could have a bearing on agate genesis. *(When reading the chapter, it is important to bear in mind that* ***amorphous silica, opal A, opal A', opal CT****, cristobalite, tridymite, silica K, silica X, silica Y,* ***chalcedony****, keatite, quartz, colloidal silica, silica glass are all forms of silica and could be represented by the same chemical formula* SiO_2).

6.1 Crystallisation from glass

The formation of chalcedony from silica glass has had a long history. Both Reis (1917) and Liesegang (1915) mention the work of the French experimental mineralogist Daubrée who in 1880 allowed various solutions to react with bottle glass at red heat. According to Liesegang, chalcedony and quartz were observed. However, Liesegang dismissed the experiment as inapplicable to agate genesis because of the high temperature needed to form the glass precursor.

In more recent times, Nacken (1948) allowed silica glass to be attacked by super heated steam at 400°C and used the chalcedony formation as a model for his theory of agate genesis. More detailed and prolonged investigation of the conditions for the **hydrothermal** conversion of silica glass were carried out by Corwin and his co-workers in the fifties (1949, 1953, 1957 I to V, 1958). The early papers established that alkaline conditions were required for the isothermal growth of quartz. Later, quartz had been grown from a solution containing the F^- and HF^- ions and these ions provided an alternative mechanism for the dissolution of silica glass via SiF_6^{2-}. The conversion of silica glass by sodium hydroxide, water, various mineral acids and buffered salt solutions was also investigated with experimental operating conditions around 400°C and 340 atm pressure. No reaction was observed with mineral acids or pure water but cristobalite (*a form of silica*) was formed in weak alkaline conditions and, with an increasing concentration of sodium hydroxide, the conversion was entirely quartz.

Corwin et al. suggested that if the dissolution goes via the $H_3SiO_4^-$ **ion** then cristobalite is formed. More basic solutions increase the ionisation of silicic acid as $H_2SiO_4^{2-}$ and quartz is formed. The 1958 paper described the effect of **alkaline metal earth** ions under hydrothermal conditions and this reaction is of interest as Linck and Heinz (1930) considered that the alkaline earths would be present as impurities in agate.

Following a synthesis of fibrous germania, White et al. (1958) produced synthetic chalcedony from silica glass that had been subject to hydrothermal solutions at 400°C and 340 atm pressure. The conversion only occurred in weakly alkaline conditions with the transformation proceeding from:

$$\underset{\text{glass}}{SiO_2} \longrightarrow \underset{\text{cristobalite}}{SiO_2} \longrightarrow \underset{\text{keatite}}{SiO_2} \longrightarrow \underset{\text{chalcedony}}{SiO_2} \longrightarrow \underset{\text{quartz}}{SiO_2}$$

Synthetic chalcedony had the same anomalous properties as natural chalcedony: brown colour in transmitted light and a **refractive index** lower than quartz.

6.1 Abstract: The work on the hydrothermal crystallisation of glass showed that quartz can only form after the glass has passed through a number of unstable forms. Fibrous quartz (agate or chalcedony) could only survive under alkaline conditions, low pressure and a temperature below 300°C .

6.2 Crystallisation from a silica gel at temperatures > 100 °C

Reports of the **hydrothermal** transformation of gelatinous silica are rare in geological literature. One such study was carried out by Oehler (1976) who found that **silica gel**, in initially neutral conditions at 100°C to 300°C and at a pressure of 3 000 atm crystallised to quartz as chalcedonic **spherulites** from experiments lasting up to seven months. No intermediate phases were detected and the chalcedony was either length fast or slow or both.

Scanning electron micrographs suggest a three-stage process with a slow induction period followed by a rapid spherulitic growth and finally a decrease in growth rate as quartz is formed.

6.2 Abstract: Oehler showed that chalcedony could be obtained from gelatinous silica that is heated up to 300°C and held at a high pressure.

6.3 Crystallisation from solution

Morey et al. (1962) obtained supersaturated solutions of silica by the continuous agitation of quartz grains for about a year. The subsequent fall to 6 mg/l after a further thirty days lead to the conclusion that the quartz was precipitated and that its maximum solubility was given as 6 mg/l at 25°C and one atmosphere pressure. Using silica as low as 0.5 mg/l, Harder and Flehmig (1970) found that silica from such under saturated solutions could still be absorbed by precipitates of iron, aluminium and magnesium hydroxides. The silica enriched precipitates at a temperature range 0-80°C formed quartz within days. Mackenzie and Gees (1971) could precipitate quartz from a solution containing 4.4 mg/l silica at 20°C. Quartz growth on the existing quartz grains was confirmed within three years using the SEM.

This work on quartz growth, under earth surface conditions, shows that the precipitation of silica as quartz is favoured when the silica concentration is saturated only with respect to quartz but is under saturated with respect to **amorphous silica**: less than 10 mg/l silica.

6.3 Abstract: Quartz can form directly from very dilute silica solutions under normal earth surface conditions. However, these conditions are not allowing the formation of ***chalcedony****.*

6.4 Crystallisation of amorphous silica

The development of continuous heating X-ray diffraction techniques in the fifties lead to a succession of papers that re-examined phase transformations within the silica system. All these papers quote operating temperatures greater than 300°C but the higher temperature could be regarded merely as rate increasing factor for the crystallisation of **amorphous silica**.

a) *Crystallisation of silica at temperatures greater than 100°C*

Birks and Schulman (1950) investigated the effect of various **alkaline earth metal** and **alkali metal** carbonates on the crystallisation of amorphous silica. They found that the alkaline earth impurities (Ca,Mg) in a ratio of 0.25 to 10 **mole** % favoured the crystallisation of amorphous silica into quartz. **Alkali metal** carbonates (Na,K) when greater than one mole percent accelerate the formation of cristobalite but were not effective in forming quartz.

The late fifties and sixties produced a switch in emphasis as investigators studied the hydrothermal crystallisation of amorphous silica. Using a temperature range of 330 to 450°C and pressures greater than 1 000 atm, Carr and Fyfe (1958) found that quartz was not formed from amorphous silica under hydrothermal conditions until two other phases had been produced. Their order of crystallisation was:

$$SiO_2 \longrightarrow SiO_2 \longrightarrow SiO_2 \longrightarrow SiO_2$$

Amorphous silica — cristoballite — silica K — quartz.

Over the specified conditions it was found that pressure had a greater effect than temperature.

Using a variety of amorphous silica starting materials, Heydemann(1964) found a new silica phase- silica X forming before cristobalite. Alkaline solutions and a temperature in the range 100 to 250°C could produce quartz within a few hours. Mizutani (1966) using the same amorphous silica and a similar temperature range but a higher constant pressure, 97 atm, found that silica X was not formed under these conditions. However, he did find quartz grains with a spherulitic texture were obtained. The rate studies suggested that the slow rate determining step is due to a solid state re-ordering of the Si−O bond as amorphous silica converts to cristobalite. Any further change to quartz required a precipitation from solution.

6.4a) Abstract: The alkaline hydrothermal conversion of amorphous silica to quartz follows a similar path to the conversion of silica glass (6.1).

b) *Crystallisation of silica at temperatures below 100 °C*

Flocculation of colloidal silica can be achieved by a variety of methods including a change in **pH**, decrease in temperature or the addition of metal hydroxides. Changing conditions can result in the formation of silica **sols** from the more stable monosilicic acid.

Silica polymers achieve stability due to the external silanol (Si−OH) groups carrying a negative charge that creates a repulsion between particles. Addition of metal hydroxides with a positive charge allows flocculation because of a bridging effect that forms larger, open structured particles (Iler, 1979). Changes that occur from the gel to the amorphous powder have received less attention than the diagenesis of the amorphous state.

Progressive diagenesis (*changes that take place at low temperature and pressure after deposition)* of **biogenic amorphous silica** has been well documented in the field and experimental studies of Mizutani 1977, Pisciotto 1981, Isaacs 1982 and many others. The general reaction is given as:

SiO_2	→	SiO_2	→	SiO_2	→	SiO_2
opal-A		**opal-A'**		**opal-CT**		quartz.

(Opal-A is the biogenic form; opal-A' is the non-biogenic form, Hein et al.1978)

X-ray diffraction patterns, in particular, enable the diagenetic sequence to be followed. Modern X-ray instruments are automated and minerals can be identified from the sharp 2θ peaks that are converted into diagnostic lattice distances.

6.4 b) Abstract: Field and experimental studies show that any conversion of ***amorphous silica*** *into agate at normal earth surface conditions would entail a number of steps. Any discussion on agate genesis that starts from amorphous silica must take these changes into account.*

6.5 A geological time scale for the conversion of amorphous silica into quartz

---

It is impossible to predict precise times for the conversion of **amorphous silica** into quartz. The type of host rock, impurities, chemical conditions, temperature, and pressure can all vary for each situation. Furthermore, each variable would alter throughout the geological time of a conversion process. Recent studies (Hesse, 1988) on deep sea sediments suggest the following:

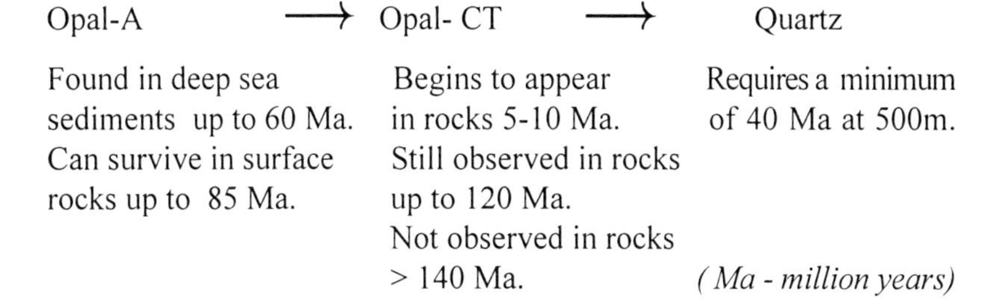

Opal-A →	Opal- CT →	Quartz
Found in deep sea sediments up to 60 Ma. Can survive in surface rocks up to 85 Ma.	Begins to appear in rocks 5-10 Ma. Still observed in rocks up to 120 Ma. Not observed in rocks > 140 Ma.	Requires a minimum of 40 Ma at 500m.

(Ma - million years)

However, different conditions can produce a dramatic reduction in the time scale: a **silica gel** containing Mg^{2+} and stored at room temperature at an initial pH of 8.2 was starting to convert into opal-CT after fourteen years (Moxon, 1996).

Chapter 7 The Development of Hypotheses on Agate Genesis since the Eighteenth Century

7.1. 1776 to1900. Silica deposition from a solution with entry through the infiltration canal

In 1776, Collini suggested that iron compounds were the cause of the red colour in agate and, in addition, the green and brown colours in moss agate. He showed that moss agate contained a magnetic material and dismissed any ideas that the substance could be organic. The possibility that the colouration in moss agate might be due to petrified moss had still to be denied some eighty years later. Collini argued that the different coloured agates were due to the circulation of iron compounds from the neighbouring rock that can penetrate the still soft agate. As the agate hardened, further penetration by the iron compounds became impossible.

Lasius (1789) and von Buch (1824) proposed that the silica entered the **vesicles** (*gas cavities*) as an aqueous solution and von Buch's description of the volcanic events leading up to the deposition of agate was acknowledged by Noeggerath (1849).

In 1849, Noeggerath and Haidinger published a series of open letters in which they stated their opposing views on the entry of the silica solution into the vesicle. The conference records, 20th July 1849, of the *Freunden der Naturwissenshaften* in Vienna stated the areas of agreement as well as their differences. Both agreed that the gaseous bubbles are formed in the erupted lava and the subsequent parallel flows were due to the movement of the lava. The misshapen **amygdale**s (*solid nodules*) are the result of an overlap between the vapour bubbles within the high viscosity lava. Noeggerath emphasised that the variation in the material of the amygdale is a feature of each particular environment. He observed that calcite amygdales from Westphalia had been dissolved in the upper reaches of the mountain but survived at the lower levels as percolating waters were prevented from reaching the calcite by the surrounding bedrock. Noeggerath stated that the silicic acid necessary for the agates came from hot springs that appeared after the decomposition of the melaphyre *(andesite)* but this hydrothermal activity was not the cause of the erosion. Agates had been found in compact bedrock, while entirely friable rocks were free from agates. However, it was the method of silica entry that produced the major difference of opinion between Noeggerath and Haidinger.

Haidinger maintained that 'mountain sweat' carried the silica to be deposited successively in the vesicle but Noeggerath, while acknowledging that water can pass through dense rock, did not accept that solutions could permeate through the alternating white layers of agate. He pointed to the **infiltration** canals as the means by which successive layers entered the vesicle (Fig 7.1).

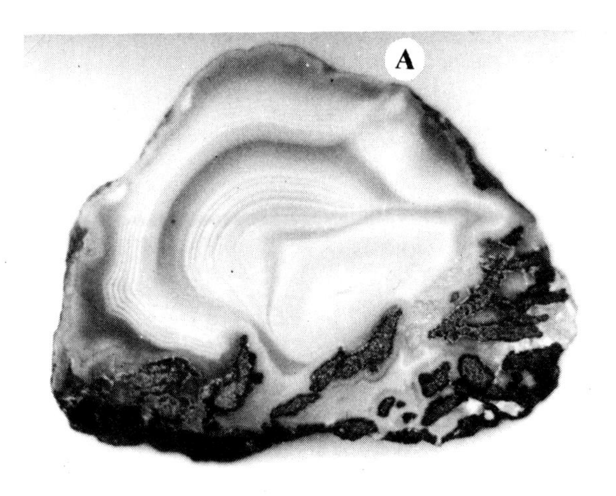

Fig. 7.1 Infiltration canal (A) in Tayport agate. Actual size.

At the end of his open letter of May 1849 Noeggerath writes,

> I beg you to compare the permeable and impermeable alternating layers that allow the art of colouring banded quartz. How is it possible for the sweating to happen and form successive precipitations from outside to in when the earliest formed impermeable layer presents a barrier to all further formations?

Haidinger did not answer the question and the infiltration canal was regarded as a prime feature for the next sixty six years until Liesegang (1915) challenged its importance.

7.2 1900 to 1945. Further support for the infiltration canal and the experimental work of Liesegang

Mathew Foster Heddle spent many years collecting and studying the agates of the Midland Valley and in 1901 published *The Mineralogy of Scotland*. A chapter is devoted to agate, in which he discussed the many sites visited by him during his lifetime. On the question of agate genesis, Heddle introduced the possibility of **osmosis** as a means by which the siliceous solutions are forced into the vesicle. The symmetry of the bands in **fortification** agate suggested to Heddle that the solution was forced evenly into the vesicle and around the whole of the periphery. The early deposit of chalcedony acted as a membrane for the solution that,

> passed along the divergent fibres of the tridymite. After the silica had been deposited, the remaining liquid is forced out of the cavity by a fresh infiltration though the tubular openings. (*Noeggerath's infiltration canals*).

Bauer (1904) stated,

> the origin of agate **amygdales** can be deduced without much difficulty (!) from the general character and mode of occurrence.

The silica source was the neighbouring rock and only when the rock was in an advanced state of decomposition could sufficient silica form. The formation of successive layers was the result of pauses in the silica precipitation. A varying water table with hot springs gave the necessary conditions. The hot water dissolved out the silica and the resulting solution filled the cavity. A retreating water table emptied the cavities and left a film of water behind. Later evaporation produced a silica layer and repetition resulted in the complete filling of the cavity with excess solution draining out via the 'tubes of escape' *(infiltration canals)*.

Until the turn of the century, the various hypotheses were established as the result of speculation and careful examination of agate patterns. In

1915, R E Liesegang published *Die Achate* and offered an alternative mechanism for agate genesis based upon a series of simulation experiments. From this work, Liesegang suggested two essential prerequisites: a silica gel filled the cavity and later, iron solutions from the weathered lava permeated through the gel producing the rhythmic banding. Alternatively, the silica gel contained an even distribution of iron and the diffusion of carbonic acid produced the banding.

On p 20 of *Die Achate*, Liesegang described the synthesis of an **infiltration** canal formed by the diffusion of Ag^+ (*siliver* ***ion***) in a gel containing an even distribution of CrO_4^{2-} (*chromate* ***ion***), Fig.7.2.

> An oval of Ag^+ is drawn with a glass rod from A to B and leaving the gap between A and B. The rhythmic banding now simulates an infiltration canal.

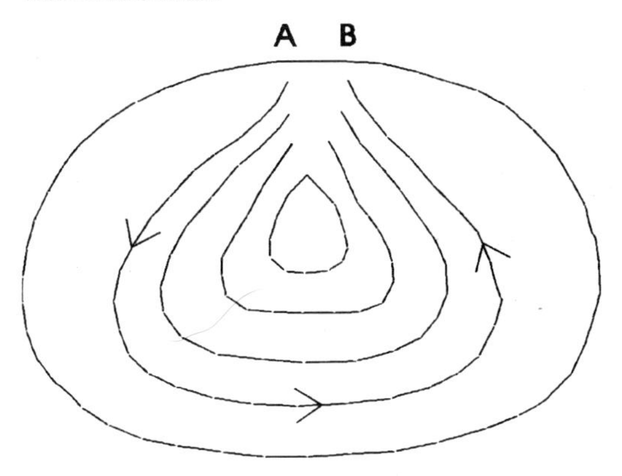

Fig. 7.2 A simulated infiltration canal. (After Liesegang, 1915)

Liesegang believed that the infiltration canals are produced whenever there is a break in the encircling iron salts.

Liesegang did not examine **thin sections** of agates and relied on the work of Hein (1907). Both believed that the crystal formation occurred at a later stage of development and after the deposition of the banding.

> In the main, the gel is converted from opal into chalcedony and finally into quartz. The crystallisation starts from the outside edge but the presence of iron compounds acts as an inhibitor for large crystal growth; they can only form when the iron compounds are removed as a precipitate.

Fossilised, Idaho opal oak wood is given as an example that shows this conversion; the vascular bundles show some opal with many containing chalcedony and only the oldest samples contained quartz.

The two main colours, based on samples from South America and Germany were given as red (iron (III) oxide, Fe_2O_3) and brown (iron (III) hydroxide, $Fe(OH)_3$). However, Liesegang cautioned his readers.

> Agate pigments are easily changed by acid, alkali, heat or even new colouring matter. Nature can also cause such changes: Brazilian agates that are partly exposed to the sun are bleached.

The pure white colours in agate were believed to depend upon the opal content. Green colours were thought to be due to iron (II) (*ferrous*) salts. Pores in chalcedony allowed the diffusion of coloured ions and made artificial staining possible.

> Such pores interconnected like a honeycomb and diffusion occurs with an aqueous medium but is prevented when the pores are blocked by opal or iron compounds. Opal prevents the dyeing of the translucent white bands in agate.

Liesegang did consider the problems that he believed remained.

> The infiltration canal is only partly explained as the canal is often filled with silica and the banding that it contains does not follow the original banding. It is difficult to explain why the canal has not been influenced by the previous effects of the pigments.

Finally, Liesegang stated that,

> the diffusion theory cannot explain every agate and there are cases when a repeated influx of silicic acid occurs. However, this is comparatively rare and the diffusion theory allows the formation of agates only when the iron compound follows the silica. If no iron compounds are available, then colourless chalcedony, opal or quartz are formed. Without this theory, one is faced with innumerable iron free and iron containing silica deposits.

In 1917, Reis published the largest single work on agate and associated minerals and followed this a year later with a further long treatise in which he gave his conclusions on the construction of agate. Observations on the first layer of chalcedony had been made by Heddle and others but Reis was the first to suggest that the thin outer layer was of a different generation. He proposed that the silica for this first generation was the result of the immediate **diagenesis** when protruding crystals of rock fragments in the vesicle were subject to erosive forces of the volcanic gases within the cavity. The second generation that formed the bulk of the agate, relied on post volcanic activity for its silica: this followed from the erosion of the melaphyre or aplite (*silica rich*) intrusions

Reis gave iron oxides a dual role: in precipitating the silica and in acting as a colouring agent for the agate. However, Reis maintained that the iron compounds entered with the silica **sol** or solution and the iron oxide was only precipitated after the silica was fully crystallised. He noted initially that there are multiple crystals competing for the available silica and as the solution becomes more dilute, so certain crystals grow at the expense of others leaving the largest crystals at the centre of the **amygdale**. Yet the work of Reis had been largely ignored until the mid fifties. Heinz (1930) is credited as the first to attack Liesegang's diffusion hypothesis. Heinz was interested in the question of banding and the amorphous nature of the white bands that proved impossible to dye artificially. Heinz' agate analysis gave an Al_2O_3/ Fe_2O_3 content at less than 1% and a silica composition greater than 97%. The various bands were examined for their opal content by boiling with 0.25M KOH for two hours. According to Heinz, an increase in density is found to correspond with an increase in opal content. X-ray analysis apparently confirmed the difficulty of dyeing opal. Heinz concluded that the bands and colour are due to the varying opal content.

These experiments allowed Linck and Heinz (1930) to suggest that the agate bands were due to alternating wet and dry seasons. The silica sol originated from the erosion of neighbouring rocks in a damp climate. Silica with alkaline earth ions (Ca^{2+} and Mg^{2+}) then passed into the cavities. In a dry climate, the sol was drawn upwards from the bottom of the rock and therefore there were two different kinds of solution. Silica deposition could form either around the cavity or flocculate and form horizontal layers.

Also in 1930, Jessop questioned the view that chalcedony was a mixture of quartz and opal since the refractive index would vary over the whole opal-quartz range: it would not be the approximately constant value that was found for chalcedony over all geological ages. However, with quartz optically positive and chalcedony optically negative, he suggested that chalcedony could be a form of silica different from both quartz and opal.

Jessop believed that the silica was deposited as gel containing both dissolved gas and solid impurities. As crystallisation advances from the outside edge, the dissolved substances would move with the crystallisation front until a point of **saturation** is reached. Any gaseous or solid impurities would be entombed in the crystallising silica and the thickness of the band depends upon the concentration of impurity and the rate of crystallisation. He suggested that the white bands contain the solid inclusions and the clear bands had the gaseous bubbles. Such a hypothesis allowed staining to be a question of retentivity and not permeability.

Liesegang (1931) published a second paper to answer the Heinz, Linck criticisms. He admitted that a pre-existing gel was not always necessary but if rhythmic deposition was to be the cause, then an inordinate amount of time would be involved.

Two further papers took a similar approach to the question of agate genesis but were diametrically opposed in their conclusions. Pilipenko (1934) and Knoll (1942) both considered the gross features of their respective collections of agate. Pilipenko argued the case for the Noeggerath hypothesis but was opposed to Liesegang's propositions, while Knoll believed the Liesegang hypothesis provided an adequate explanation.

Pilipenko cites the following points that cannot be answered by the Liesegang hypothesis:

i) Some agates have a hollow centre; this shows that the cavity is not totally filled by a gel.

ii) There is no explanation why the pigment of the bands in the same piece of agate can be different.

iii) Liesegang's artificial preparations are torn and split while in nature this phenomenon is rare.

iv) The role of pigmentation is not clear in the case of:

a) well-formed amethyst crystal centres

b) brown pigments found in various zones

c) the disappearence of strong pigment zones.

As an alternative Pilipenko stated,

> a study of the outer surfaces of agate reveals many pores or openings in the walls of sections that surround the agate; these openings allow

the silica to enter the vesicle.

Knoll reviewed the argument for the *Inflow Theory* as presented by Linck and Heinz and queried how a mechanism that depends on gravity for the entry of silica still manages to allow the formation of agate that is other than horizontally banded. He suggested that it was possible for gel fortification and layer precipitation to occur at the same time; later the solution turned to a gel with diffusion layers appearing afterwards.

7.3 1948 to 1960. Silica as glass droplets and further support for the hypothesis of Reis

In a paper that is more tentative in its suggestions than many of its predecessors, Nacken (1948) suggested that the silica existed as an impermeable liquid state within the **magma**. Perhaps, in an attempt to pre-empt the inevitable criticism, Nacken comments on the problem presented by the 1 600 °C melting point of silica existing in a 1 100 °C melting point **basaltic** magma. He suggested that a magma containing excess silica could divide into a silica rich component with a lower density than the bulk magma. These silica drops rise and eventually form agate. Once the silica glass was in place within the basalt, Nacken returned to his original synthesis of chalcedony from glass. The conversion was sensitive to **pH**, impurities and the temperature gradient within the glass that had been subject to hydrothermal conversion at 400°C. When the glass had been converted to chalcedony, there was a volume decrease that allowed further attack by the hydrothermal solution along capillary cracks. Any impurities were pushed along the crystallisation front and precipitated in layers.

Schlossmacher (1950) agreed with Nacken that agate was formed because of an acid product within the magma but thought that the silica contained water in a superheated state. He argued that the banding was the result of temperature differentiation within the glass causing different band thickness and fibre textures. The rate of crystallisation depends upon the temperature difference, with the points of nucleation competing to influence the growth of chalcedony or macroquartz. Quartz formation required a low nucleation and a high rate of crystallisation while the high nucleation and slow crystallisation allowed the chalcedonic outer layer to form.

Fischer (1954) reviewed the twentieth century German literature on agate genesis and dealt with the hypotheses of Liesegang , Nacken and Reis in some detail. After studying the bulk features of a number of agates Fischer supported the ideas of Reis and dismissed the Nacken hypothesis because:

i) a magmatic temperature of 1 100°C would not contain a melt of silica at 1 600°C.

ii) the common occurrence of calcite as a filling within the **amygdale** would result in wollastonite at the silica/ calcite contact; wollastonite has not been found.(*wollastonite is calcium silicate; formed at high temperatures from siliceous limestones*)

iii) **Pegmatite minerals** have not been found as vesicular fillings and the water containing the silica glass melt corresponds more closely to hydrothermal activity.

Liesegang's ideas were dismissed by Fischer since all his experiments demanded a pre-existing gel and he failed to link laboratory experiments with the field observations. Fischer accepted that silica had a low solubility in water but both the enormous volumes of water vapour generated during volcanic activity and the length of time for the demise of thermal springs were sufficient to support the theory of Reis.

Braitsch (1957) was primarily concerned with the orientation of the crystallographic axes in fibrous quartz but he considered the genesis of chalcedony. While dismissing the Nacken-Schlossmacher hypothesis on petrological grounds, he agreed that banding could be formed in the manner described by Reis but there was still uncertainty whether this was via silica gel or solution.

7.4 1970 to the present. The use of modern instrumentation

During this period, the use of the electron microscope lead to many papers discussing possible mechanisms for genesis based on electron micrograph observations. Sunagawa and Ohta (1976) concluded that agate was formed after three principle stages: chalcedonic wall lining, growth of quartz, the formation of horizontal bands. The last two stages may be absent. They proposed that the agate was formed from repeated entry of a silica rich solution that must have a high concentration of silica but a low viscosity so that the solution can enter the cavity through narrow ducts. Such silica solutions would be partly polymerised and coagulate as units defined as polymer blocs. Bloc nuclei coagulated by either adhering to the wall and forming a fibrous structure or forming bulky crystallites suspended in the solution. This type of crystal growth would, according to Sunagawa and Ohta, explain why chalcedony predominates as a vesicular filling while quartz is the major product of hydrothermal veins. A lack of agitation in the **vesicles** allowed the bloc nuclei to grow from the wall and form the fibrous structure whereas the hydrothermal veins are open and the bloc nuclei coagulate in solution and can settle when they reach critical size.

Detailed modern chemical analysis of agate is rare in literature but Flörke et al. (1982) investigated seven Brazilian agates for the trace impurities and water content as free molecular water and OH groups *(attached to silicon as Si−OH)*. Using chemical analysis and water composition differences they could distinguish two types of deposited silica within horizontal banded agate and suggested genesis based upon an initial precipitate from supercritical fluids with the deposition of the horizontal layers following at a later stage (*for pure water the supercritical temperature is > 374°C but dissolved solutes would elevate this temperature considerably.*) Graetsch et al. (1985) using similar methods suggested that the temperature of formation was < 250°C.

Further attempts have been made to try to establish the temperature of agate genesis using oxygen isotope analysis. (*Oxygen* ***isotopes*** *^{16}O and ^{18}O, together with the hydrogen isotopes ^{1}H and ^{2}H allow a prediction of the nature and likely temperature at formation of any encapsulated water)*. Blankenburg and co-workers (1981,1982,1983) used ^{18}O and a crystallite size geothermometer to suggest agate formation temperatures of > 375°C with genesis based on the remelting of **chert xenoliths**. This proposition requires the recycling of sedimentary cherts after melting within a molten magma and an eventual crystallisation as agate. Fallick et al. (1985) and Harris (1989) using oxygen isotope analysis on Midland Valley and South African agates respectively believed that their separate data showed the temperature of agate genesis at ~50°C and 120°C.

Landmesser (1984) gave a detailed review (the text is in German) of the hypotheses on agate genesis. In 1988, he also argued that the only physiochemical process to account for agate formation must take place in a low pressure/temperature range. Such a P-T field of sedimentation and **diagenesis** requires the initial silica to be a dispersed silica system; this would include the monomeric, polymeric forms of silica and colloidal silica. It is assumed that the gel-like zones formed the eventual chalcedonic **spherulites**. In a later paper (1992), Landmesser discussed silica transportation through the host rock as silicic acid $Si(OH)_4$ and proposed genesis at a temperature less than 200°C.

Moxon (1991) using optical and electron micrograph observations, suggested genesis based on the theory of spherulitic crystallisation developed by Keith and Padden (1963,1964a, 1964b). The application of this theory allowed fibres to develop during the crystallisation from high silica polymers while rejecting the low polymers and monomers of silicic acid. Heaney (1993) proposed that chalcedonic growth occurs from short chain polymers via bridging monomers at temperatures of < 100° C.

Harder (1993) discussed agate formation on the basis of experimental results involving the mixing of aluminium and/or iron hydroxides with high concentration silica **sols**. The proposed mechanism then invoked a mixing within the **vesicle** of an alkaline silica sol with a low pH surface solution. The mixed product was described as having a gel-like primary texture similar to agate. He suggested that the gel lined the cavity while the solution diffused through the porous agate. Climatic events would lead to the cavity being filled and diagenetic crystallisation processes would result in the eventual formation of agate.

Chapter 7. Abstract: Essentially, the hypotheses propose that the silica enters the vesicle either in true solution or as a gel. The banding in agate is caused either by external factors that can produce separate rhythmic deposits or internal organisation generating the banding from a single crystallisation process.

Hypotheses of Agate Genesis

(Not all hypotheses on the silica sources and cause of the banding are easily categorised but a general summary of the views expressed by the interested authors is given below)

Source - the result of:

True solution	**or**	***Silica Gel***
(H_4SiO_4) 1,6,7,9,11. 15,19,20,23.		(Gel-like silica with a large molecular mass) 2,3,4,5,8,10,16,22.
or		High temperature deposit 17,18, 21.
Glass 12,13,14.		

+ → **Agate**

Banding- caused by:

Internal Factors	**or**	***External Factors***
(describe the process of crystallisation from a single silica deposit) 6,9,11,12,13, 14,21,22.		(produce banding from repeated silica deposits) 3,4,5,7,8,10,15, 16,17,18,19,20.

1) Lasius,1789; 2) von Buch,1824; 3) Noeggerath,1849; 4) Haidinger,1849; 5) Heddle,1901; 6) Liesegang,1915,1931; 7) Reis,1917; 8) Linck, Heinz, 1930; 9) Jessop,1931; 10) Pilipenko,1934; 11) Knoll,1942: 12) Nacken,1948; 13) Schlossmacher,1950; 14) Blankenburget al.,1981,1982,1983; 15) Fischer,1954; 16) Sunagawa,Ohta,1976; 17) Flörke etal.1982; 18) Graetsch, 1985; 19) Landmesser, 1988,1992; 20) Harder, 1993; 21) Moxon, 1991; 22) Wang and Merino, 1990; 23) Heaney, 1993.

Chapter 8 Agate Genesis - a discussion

Unfortunately, it cannot be said that any consensus on the question of agate genesis has slowly evolved over the last two hundred years. Too many questions on the range of temperature and pressure, the type and source of silica sol/ solution and the mechanism of the crystallisation need to be fully answered before the story of agate genesis can be regarded as having been solved. In this chapter, discussion of genesis will be limited to the problems of **fortification** agate.

8.1 Liesegang Phenomenon.

Liesegang's (1915,1931) experiments do produce effects that are superficially very similar to the banding in agate and surprisingly many texts on geochemistry continue to link the Liesegang rings and agate genesis (eg Krauskopf and Bird, 1995). Scientific journals have not been so kind and there have been few supporters since the first 1915 paper.

Liesegang does not give any conditions for the formation of the pre-existing gel that is required before banding can occur. Both text and later paper concentrate on the gross features of the agate and simulated gel experiments. Petrographic thin sections occupy less than a page in the whole of *Die Achate* and are taken from the work of Hein (1908).

Liesegang relegates thin section observations as secondary to the gross features and he says on p 22,

> One could fill a book if one studied the different structures of agate. Leaving the differences in the background, it seems better to emphasise the genetic possibilities.

Yet by concentrating on the gross features, Liesegang has ignored many problems that require clarification. There is no clear explanation for the formation of quartz centres in agate geodes. On p 26,

> The series gel to opal to chalcedony to quartz is followed but the process can be halted at any of the stages.

On this basis, one accepts a description of chalcedony as a metastable form of quartz and time alone prevents the conversion of chalcedony into quartz. However on p 23, in an attempt to explain quartz geodes, Liesegang invokes the protective colloid effect: by which the iron compounds prevent the crystallisation of quartz.

> Only when the iron has been removed can the quartz form.

If the gel has already been banded, one has to ask, how can the iron behave as a protective colloid in the centre of the agate and for that matter in the iron-free areas between the bands where granular quartz would also be expected to form?

Isemura (1939) investigated the conditions that can alter the rhythmic precipitation and showed the limits for ring formation. Generally, bands only form over narrow concentration limits of inner electrolyte. The concentration of the outer electrolyte must be higher, preferably by several orders of magnitude, than that of the inner electrolyte. If the concentrations are too great, then the precipitation becomes continuous. Again could such constraints lead to the world wide formation of agate? Liesegang linked the white bands to the concentration of opal but he makes no further comment on the mechanism of the formation of the iron-free agates. However, the major weakness in Lisegang's hypothesis is his failure to acknowledge the high percentage of water in the silica gel which on dehydration would leave only 5% of the bulk: a total collapse of the banded structure.

The current standing of the Liesegang hypothesis as an explanation for agate genesis in English language texts is curious. It is, I believe, the novelty of the Liesegang's experiments and the difficulties of translation of many early German papers that has allowed Liesegang's observations to continue as a major theory of agate genesis.

8.2 Formation from a silica melt.

Direct crystallisation of **magmatic** silica would provide the neatest explanation for the silica source. Unfortunately, a further several hundred degrees Celsius would be required if silica was to exist in molten magma. This problem was appreciated by Nacken (1948) who first suggested the concept. Schlossmacher (1950) refined the idea with temperature differentiation being invoked for band formation but he made no comment on the difficulties of the mechanism. Fischer (1954) drew attention to the fact that wollastonite had not been detected at any calcite chalcedony contact and the absence of normal **pegmatite minerals** provided further objections. Nacken's own experimental work and the more detailed investigation by White and Corwin (1961) show that the hydrothermal devitrification of silica glass proceeds via cristobalite to keatite to chalcedony and finally quartz. As it is the outside edge of the supposed silica droplet that is most subject to superheated steam one would expect that quartz would be on the circumference with a chalcedonic centre; the reality is the reverse.

Blankenburg and co-workers (1981, 1982, 1983) discussed the idea of re-melted **chert xenoliths** as the silica source. Again, this avoids the difficulty of seeking an external silica source but at the very least, it still has the major problem of explaining why the silica once molten should remain in this immiscible state to re-emerge in a later volcanic flow and re-crystallise as agate.

8.3 The Inflow Theory

In its basic form the *Inflow Theory* can be regarded as the deposition of silica from a solution or sol into the empty vesicle. Since 1915, each proponent of this hypothesis has been united in opposition to Liesegang while adding his own refinement. While the first suggestion of a silica solution appears to have been made by Lasius (1789) it was the open discussion between Noeggerath and Haidinger in 1849 that summarised the previous knowledge. This lead to the acceptance of the **infiltration canal** as the means by which silica solutions enter the vesicle. But since the turn of the century others (Pilipenko, 1934; Macpherson, 1989) have emphasised the importance of this feature as a tube of escape.

This author has sliced a few hundred Scottish agates, many into several sections with a few to destruction and the number of infiltration canals observed are very limited. A similar ratio was obtained by Smith(1910) who with Heddle (1901) list the characteristics of this rare but interesting feature in the Scottish agates. Agate 71(Fig. 7.1) from Tayport shows an infiltration canal that has a depth of about 1 cm along the outer crust. Although the inner bands in agate 71 are continuous, they are frequently broken and always point to the outer edge. Smith notes and my limited samples would confirm the fact that the canals never breach the outermost layer. In spite of which, the direction of the bands must point to the feature as a method of escape rather than entry.

Heddle (1901) suggested that the outer layer acts as a membrane for osmosis. The idea was recently revived when Pettijohn (1975) offered osmosis as a mechanism for the formation of chert nodules. Heddle's description of the process is not clear and the direction of osmotic pressure would be the opposite to that required.

> The silica is deposited through successive layers that continue to allow osmotic pressure to act. After crystallisation, the solvent is forced out through the tubes of escape by the entrance of fresh strong solution according to the laws of endosmose.

Osmosis is the passage of solvent through a semi-permeable membrane from a solution of low concentration to one of high concentration; it is difficult to visualise how osmosis would help even if the membrane were complete. It seems that Heddle is describing diffusion. Nevertheless, once the tube of escape has formed, any incoming fresh silica solution would be just as free to leave as the solvent.

Bauer (1901) provides an interesting alternative by using the varying water table with hot silica springs.

> The hot water dissolves the silica from the surrounding rock and fills up the cavity. When the water level falls, the cavities are emptied and

> subsequent evaporation leaves a thin layer of silica. Repetition of the process results in the complete filling of the cavity and excess solution drains out of the tubes of escape.

Leaving aside the complex patterns of many agates and limiting discussion to the repetition banding of a simple fortification agate, Bauer, together with others who argue this hypothesis, credit the natural forces with an abnormal degree of selectivity. Apparently, many separate deposits can constitute a single colourless band to be followed by many iron-containing depositions that constitute the coloured band. This alternation of events must continue, in defiance of gravity, until the agate is full.

Apart from the improbability of such a sequence, the impermeability of white bands has been discussed by Noeggerath, 1849; Liesegang, 1915 and Jessop, 1930. If fresh solutions could permeate the older layers before crystallisation, then one would expect the older amorphous layers to be stained by pigment carrying solutions.

Heinz (1930) tried to relate the question of banding to the possible amorphous nature of the white bands. The relationship between density and opal content as developed by Heinz agreed with the hypothesis current at the time: chalcedony was a mixture of quartz and **opal**. Since 1922, many workers have found that chalcedony always gives a quartz X-ray diffraction pattern. However, the question of its opal content was not clarified until Midgley (1951) using DTA, surface area determinations and Folk and Weaver (1952) using the electron microscope solved the problem of the opal content. They explained that the properties of chalcedony were due to small **inclusions**.However, recent extensive examinations of chert, agate, and non-banded chalcedony have now revealed the presence of a new form of silica identified as moganite (Heaney and Post,1992). The detection of moganite within chalcedony requires sophisticated X-ray techniques or the use of dark field transmission electron microscopy. Moganite is described as an alternate stacking of slices of left and right hand quartz on the unit cell scale (Graetsch, 1994). Further investigations are showing differences of moganite compositions in agate world wide and could eventually lead to further progress in the story of agate genesis.

Sunagawa and Ohta (1976) attempted a unified explanation for the formation of fibrous chalcedony, macro and microquartz. Their suggested silica source is,

> the natural silica containing hydrothermal solution that repeatedly enters the cavity as a low viscosity solution through narrow ducts.

Their crystallisation mechanism is based upon the bloc nuclei concept by which selective units up to 1 000 Å are formed around impurity ions to be placed as larger building blocks for the formation of chalcedony. Sunagawa and Ohta do not suggest possible temperatures or silica concentrations. The concept of bloc nuclei was developed for ionic systems and the straightforward silica **polymerisation** would seem sufficient in this case. The present day 'natural silica containing hydrothermal solutions' are not any more viscous than water in that the silica they contain is primarily monomeric silicic acid in a concentration range of 360 to 420 mg/l (White et al., 1956). Hot springs on cooling deposit the silica as gelatinous flocs. Again there is the difficulty of repeated entry through crystallised chalcedony and Sunagawa and Ohta do not enlarge upon the narrow ducts.

Fischer (1954) felt that the large volumes of water emitted during volcanic and post volcanic activity were sufficient to sustain the repeated inflow of silica solution. This proposition would perhaps be acceptable if agate was only found, like quartz veins, in open fissures. White (1955) and White et al., (1956) showed that the hot springs in the USA are considerably under saturated with respect to **amorphous silica**. Geyserite and chalcedonic sinter were being deposited in and around the hot springs. Although there is no direct evidence of the conversion of opal into chalcedony, bore holes suggest that it is happening. Interestingly chalcedony was not recognised in the hot spring sinter or near surface veins. These comments concur with later field and experimental studies (Mizutani, 1977; Pisciotto, 1981; Isaacs, 1982 and others). However, zonal distributions in the field do not explain either the continuous fibrosity in agate or the restructuring of low density **amorphous silica** into compact chalcedony within a vesicle without a further supply of silica.

Davies (1964), in a review of published chemical analyses of stream and groundwaters, concluded that while silica can range from 3 mg/l in lakes derived from recent snow to 4 000 mg/l in a Californian stream it has a variability less than any other major constituent: a median value for silica would be 17 mg/l for stream water and 14 mg/l for groundwater. Also Alaskan groundwaters (0-5 °C) show only minor variations with tropical groundwaters (25-35 °C). Laboratory studies show it is the rock type rather than temperature (0-30° C range) that has a greater influence on the solubility of silica. If a silica concentration of 20 mg/l is taken, then an agate of 100 g would require a minimum volume of 5 000 l. However, given the geological time scale it could be argued that this volume of water would not be a problem. Leaching could be a possible source for the silica.

Water in equilibrium with quartz produces a silica solubility of less than 10 mg/l while the amorphous forms can have a solubility up to 130 mg /l (Iler, 1979). **Feldspars** and clay minerals produce values between these two extremes (Sicvcr,1962). Field observations by Tedrow and Wilkerson (1953) showed that alkali and alkaline earth ions are the first particles to be leached from **igneous** rocks during the early stages of chemical weathering in tropical and temperate climates. The ions are found mainly in the feldspars and **ferromagnesian** minerals of relative low stability towards weathering. The leaching of iron from parent rocks is limited by the low solubility of Fe^{3+} and the higher solubility of its host minerals. However, when iron is present as Fe^{2+} the minerals are relatively unstable but the iron appears unlikely to travel far. Navrot and Singer (1976) found that only a limited part of the iron was leached from the basic igneous rocks during clay formation and that much of it was incorporated in the clay fraction. Losses of silica require intensive leaching due to the low solubility of the mineral although acid weathering accelerates the loss.

The possibility that **incongruent dissolution** is responsible for the high purity of the agate amygdale is discounted by the experimental work of Huang and Keller (1970). They found that the surface in **augite** is slightly enriched by silica but very markedly by iron and aluminium. The breakdown of the **feldspars** results in a surface that is rich in aluminium and to a lesser extent in silica while it becomes depleted in the **alkali metals**. Altered olivine has been frequently observed in the agate bearing lavas of the Midland Valley but the magnesium content is only slightly slower than silica in its dissolution. With field and experimental evidence on leaching it is considered that the silica source cannot be due to this process near the vesicle because:

a) samples of agate-bearing lava have feldspars that show no alteration.

b) there is no evidence of mineral loss from the glassy residuum in the groundmass. It is often filled with iron dust and is dark brown or black but in thin section there is no obvious sign of alteration: it is free from cracks and kaolinite. In addition, there is no residual block structure that characterises weathering.

c) the ferromagnesian minerals are always altered but if these were to be the source of the silica, then it would be expected that Fe^{3+} would always be at a much higher level than the 0.011 % found by Flörke et al.(1982). But the large volume of water necessary to carry the silica formed by leaching at a distance is also discounted. Such a process would have resulted in an erosion around the vesicle.

Hypotheses based on an **amorphous silica** precursor begin with either a dehydrated gel or the direct precipitation of amorphous silica whose deposition depends upon the rhythmic occurrences in nature. The many variables of starting materials, pH, fluid pressure, temperature and particle size make constructive speculation difficult. However, the conversion of amorphous silica into quartz is at least a two-stage process when:

$$\text{Opal A} \longrightarrow \text{Opal CT} \longrightarrow \text{Quartz}$$

The transformation of gelatinous silica to opal CT involves at least two further intermediate stages that could also form via a dissolution and reprecipitation mechanism (Moxon, 1996). Whether or not silica X or Y is formed depends upon the conditions and as such could offer an alternative route for the formation of quartz.

Whatever the kinetics of the reaction, the final step has to show a viable mechanism for the formation of fibrous quartz. Given an **amygdale** filled with **amorphous silica**, it would be expected that such a porous system would be susceptible to multiple nucleation and prevent the growth of the large fibres that are the most characteristic texture of chalcedony in agate. However, one further major objection to an amorphous silica conversion at temperatures of 25-100°C has to be the density differences between amorphous silica and chalcedony: a further 18% of silica would be necessary if the amygdale is to remain completely full.

Unlike chert, evidence for the formation of agate starting from amorphous silica is slight and without a viable mechanism to explain the formation of fibrous chalcedony. Agate and **chert** do have many similarities and some consideration should be given to the extensive field studies and laboratory experiments that have been carried out in an attempt to solve the origin of chert.

8.4 Chert

Agate and chert are linked as members of the microcrystalline family of quartz minerals and both can have a silica composition up to 98%. Chert is the group name used for a variety of sedimentary siliceous deposits whose major component is re-constituted silica (flint is used to describe chert that is found in the chalk of western Europe at the time of the **Upper Cretaceous**). Chert genesis has had a long history of investigation but, unlike agate, it has attracted a wide interest in the scientific community. There are a number of reasons for the increased attention, not least the vast deposits of chert together with the link between ancient siliceous organisms and early forms of life.

The conversion of siliceous skeletons into chert is a long, complex process and the starting point of much chert genesis is based upon the conversion of radiolarian and diatomaceous silica (opal-A) into opal-CT and finally into quartz. This chert connection with agate would be a further link if non-biogenic **amorphous silica** was the precursor for agate. Detailed discussion of this mechanism has been considered in 8.3 but there are examples where chert formation is not **biogenic** in origin.

The alkaline lakes at Lake Magadi, Kenya allow the formation of cherts as replacements for the precipitated sodium silicates: magadiite and kenyaite. Scientific interest continues with these Magadi cherts as they are the only known examples of non-biogenic chert and detailed studies could throw more light on the origin of **Precambrian** silica rocks.

Schubel and Simonson (1990) have modified earlier hypotheses on the origin of the Magadi deposits and suggested that genesis was the result of an early conversion of magadiite to chert by leaching brines, to be followed by a later washing of fresh water. These cherts have produced a distinctive grid-like microscopic orientation of the quartz crystals. Schubel and Simonson suggested that this texture appeared to have evolved from the magadiite precursor. However, these distinctive structures have not been observed in agate.

Chert is the world's oldest sedimentary rock and there is much discussion amongst sedimentologists over the silica source and the method of formation of these Precambrian rocks that could not have a **biogenic** origin. According to Knauth (1994), the giant Onverwacht chert deposits in South Africa could have utilised the silica from volcanic glass and **pyroclastic** debris. However, an intense silicification from overlying volcanic products as a silica source for agate has to be rejected as the silica solutions would be simply lost as a run-off to the surrounding environment.

8.5 Celadonite coating

Many agates found on the beach and nearly all agates taken from lava have a thin wash of **celadonite**. The mineral is regarded as the first lining on the vesicle wall formed from the alteration of the ferromagnesian constituents. A few Scottish agates that have been partially exposed to the elements show how easily the wash can be removed. One wonders, that if the celadonite was a first coating, why the later introduction of silica does not bring the green earth into the vesicle. A few agates have 'islands' of lava surrounded by a 'sea' of agate (Fig.7.1) and these lava fragments are still covered by a celadonite coat. This celadonite could not enter before crystallisation. One alternative is that the celadonite appears as an alteration product after crystallisation of the silica and fills the minute crack separating the agate from the vesicle wall or the lava fragments from the agate.

8.6 First generation chalcedony

Scottish agates universally reveal an apparent first generation of chalcedony that has a depth of approximately 1 to 2 mm. If this initial layer is not apparent in the hand specimen, it becomes obvious when viewed in thin section with the polars crossed. Reis (1917) was the first worker to recognise this feature. As with the **celadonite** coating, this observation can also be made around the 'islands' of lava surrounded by a 'sea' of agate (Fig. 7.1). Clearly this cannot be a first generation and it would appear that the silica has an initial reaction with the vesicle wall. If hydroxide ions are present in the wall, it produces the rarely observed length slow chalcedony.

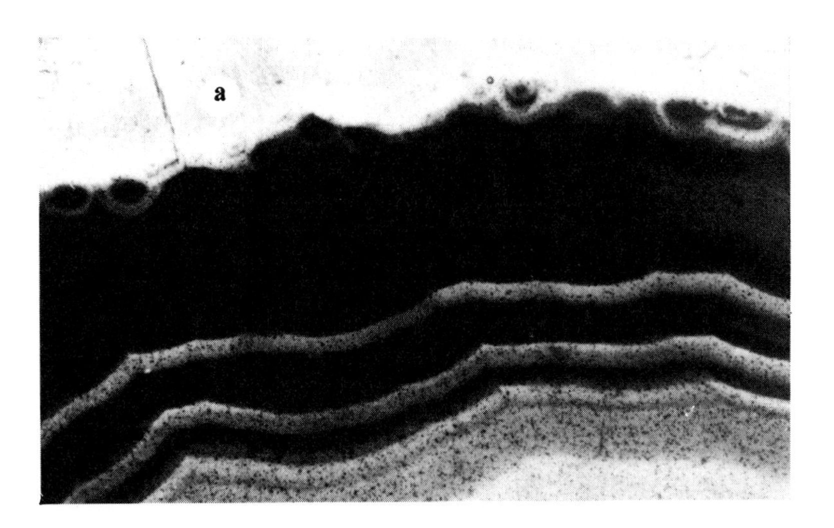

Fig. 8.1A pink, white and clear banded agate shows the difference between the 'first generation' (a) and subsequent banding. The band (a) is totally devoid of any iron oxide spots. However, it can be argued that the initial crystallisation front has rejected the iron oxide until it reaches a high enough concentration for precipitation to occur. Carrick Hills, Ayrshire. Short edge represents 2 mm. (x 30, crossed polars).

Chapter 9 From vesicle to agate amygdale

9.1 A possible mechanism

The uncertainty of laboratory data applied to the final stages of magmatic crystallisation can only make any discussion of agate genesis highly speculative. Beside the usual variables of temperature, pressure, time and type of mineralising solution one has the added problems of the unique nature of every agate and limited scientific interest producing few published field observations.

The release of magma onto the earth's surface means a drastic reduction in the confining pressure and the formation of gas bubbles containing volatiles of various compositions. Analyses of modern volcanic gaseous emissions show water vapour frequently reaching 90% of the total gaseous content. Whatever the initial gas content, the agates record their final form and often show a stretched shape elongated by the lava flow. Occasionally the **vesicles** have touched, providing some more unusual shapes.

Gas bubbles continue to rise through the magma until the final stage of crystallisation and further expansion of the bubbles is possible.This effect is revealed in thin section when the **feldspar** laths next to the vesicle show that a greater proportion are tangential to the cavity, while the feldspars in the groundmass are arranged randomly. In addition, with limited fluidity in the groundmass, the vesicle can burst and form stringers; this was a feature observed in a spilite lava (Hopgood, 1962). Stringers have been observed in this study and were later filled with small quartz grains showing **undulose extinction**,.

A typical agate bearing lava flow on the west or east coast of the Midland Valley shows a zonal arrangement of the amygdaloidal minerals within the flow. Generally, there is an empty honeycomb at a slaggy top and beneath this, a small proportion of the vesicles are filled with agate or calcite. The majority frequently contain celadonite or a chloritic mineral. Agates are generally found in the middle to lower half of the flow. Such zonal arrangements of the mineral fillings have been frequently reported in the literature. Whitford-Stark (1973) suggested that the complete infilling of vesicles by **chlorite** in the andesites of the Borrowdale volcanics is the result of the chlorite overcoming the gas pressure during the final stage of crystallisation. Larger vesicles, with a greater gas pressure, allowed only a wall lining to occur.

Walker's (1960) detailed study of zeolites in the Antrim **basalts** showed that the silica minerals were limited to the middle of tholeiitic lava flows and were excluded from the olivine basalts. The absence of any obvious volcanic centres in these Antrim basalts lead to the suggestion that access for the silica minerals could be via faults and joints in the tholeiitic lavas. The possibility of any late stage hydrothermal activity, emanating from a volcanic centre in the Midland Valley, acting as the silica source is unlikely as the agates are flow associated and not linked to any obvious volcanic centre (Moxon, 1991). Any volcanic centres that can still be identified are many miles away from the agate lavas and it is impossible for the solutions to traverse the distance and penetrate the vesicle to deposit the silica.

The microstructure provides irrefutable evidence that crystallisation can only begin when the vesicle is totally full of silica (Fig. 9.1). If this is accepted, then the total initial silica deposit must have an overall density equal or greater than that of chalcedony: 2. 65 g/cm^3. Entry of the silica solution through ducts or cracks would mean that the imagination has to be stretched further to allow an even distribution of new banding inside previous agate layers. After deposition of the silica, that must be chalcedonic quartz, the residual solution would need to escape from what is presumably an ever increasingly crystalline vesicle. It has to be admitted that the bands do sometimes show distinct breaks but frequently the fibres breach the banding. Direct precipitation of quartz from a silica solution has only been found to occur from very low concentrations of silica. Mackenzie and Gees (1971) obtained quartz overgrowths at 20°C from a solution containing 4.4 mg/ l. This would mean that a relatively small agate nodule of 50 g would require several thousand litres to deposit all the silica as chalcedony. If the agate was evenly banded with alternating clear chalcedony and **hematite** bands, then this deposition would need to form from many iron-free silica deposits and then be followed by many iron-containing silica deposits. The whole process would need to alternate and be repeated thousands of time before filling the vesicle (*Inflow Theory*).

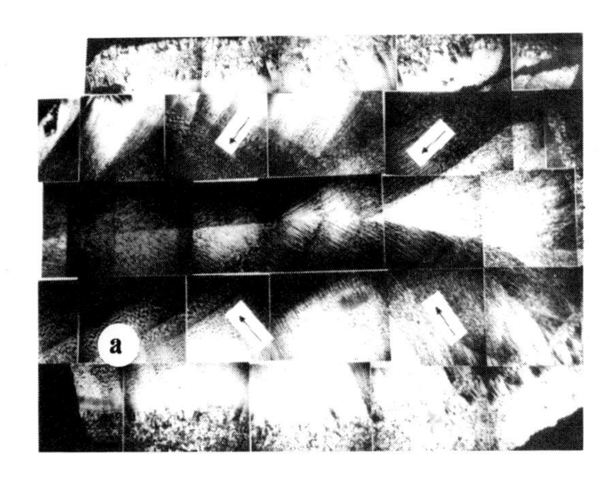

Fig. 9.1 A composite micrograph that shows a fine fibrous structure sweeping towards the centre in the direction of the arrows. The white bands (a) are just visible at this magnification (x 2.5). Brazilian agate. Short edge represents 2.2 cm.

Agates from the Midland Valley are all to be found in lavas with a high glassy residuum (Fig.1.5) and glassy rocks represent a high silica fractionation (Marshall,1961). Evidence from present day volcanic activity is limited but as agates are linked to major **orogenic** events, this is not too surprising. Naboko and Silnichenko (1957) have reported that a mobile silica gel is currently forming on the solfataras of the Golovnin volcano. The gel contains up to 52% silica and dehydrates to form opal, quartz and cristobalite.

Experimental studies have been carried out on the alkali silicate system, Na_2O-H_2O-SiO_2 , (Ganeyev, 1975 and others) and these show that an immisicibility boundary exists between the 75-90% gelatinous silica and 25-10% NaOH. X-ray diffractograms on jelly-like transparent masses show weak lines of cristobalite and less frequently quartz whose intensity increases with dehydration.

An isothermal mathematical model could account for many compositional properties of agates and show that banding self organisation would be possible for certain parameter levels that included a silica gel concentration of > 1 g /cm³ (Wang and Merino, 1990).

Over the last thirty years, a greater understanding of silica geochemistry has been made within the 0-100°C temperature range. Any proposition of agate genesis within this temperature range encounters problems discussed in 8.3. There are obvious difficulties that prevent similar progress in field studies associated with volcanic activity at high pressures and temperatures ~1000°C. In part by elimination of alternatives, it is suggested that the formation of agate would be most adequately explained by the direct deposition of a high density silica gel perhaps formed as an ooze in the final stages of the crystallising magma. There are difficulties with this proposed route and agate genesis could only take place because of the unmixing of components into a highly siliceous gel with an aqueous solution of other substances.

Keith and Padden (1963,1964a,1964b) developed a theory of spherulitic crystallisation that was based on the experimental study of long chain polymers but the principles have had a wide application in geology; particularly relevant is the spherulitic growth in quartz microspheres in gels (Oehler, 1976). Keith and Padden argued that a unified theory of spherulitic crystallisation should be possible in spite of the wide range of substances where this type of growth is found; they have a common environment of growth from a high viscosity melt or gel and a twisted fibre habit. When fibrous growth can be observed in a melt, the relationship between the velocity of crystal advance (G) and the temperature difference at the growth front (Δt) expressed as $G/\Delta t$ is in the order of 10^{-4} to 10^{-8} cm/ sec/ °C compared with the normal growth along the crystallographic axis of 1 to 100 cm/ sec/ °C. The theory demands that spherulitic growth is limited to multicomponent systems where the spherulite grows in an impure but concentrated solution of high viscosity. The need for an impure solution does not discount spherulitic growth from a pure silica gel as components with low molecular mass or branched polymers can behave as impurities to the long chained polymeric counterparts. For spherulitic crystallisation, single nuclei allow the formation of radial fibrous crystalline habits that arise from the ability of the crystals to branch at small angles from the fibres axis and an inability to follow a preferred crystallographic axis. Crystals growing from such a solution remove the pure material from the liquid and reject the impurities so that an impurity rich layer builds up at the liquid/ crystal interface. The impurity thickness of the interface δ, that is also the approximate thickness of the fibres, is governed by the impurity coefficient D and the crystal growth rate such that $\delta = D/G$.

During spherulitic growth, the impurity thickness must be small compared with the rate of crystal growth. Under such conditions, the surface of the crystal becomes irregular as projections seek the purer solutions and the impurity is rejected into the troughs caused by the projections. Growth continues in a forward direction but is prevented laterally because of the impurities between the fibres. Each fibre has a surface projection that splits into fresh fibres approximately δ in width, at a small angle to the parent fibre and slightly misaligned to each other. The theory of spherulitic crystallisation, as outlined by Keith and Padden, provides an attractive mechanism for chalcedonic growth if the initial deposit was a high density silica gel.

Fig. 9.2 shows a possible crystallisation sequence with the celadonite coating and the first generation of silica ignored. Nucleation generally starts from the outside edge, although there are many examples where nucleation has also started within the bulk of the silica (Fig.9.2a). Wherever nucleation occurs, the growth of the spherulite proceeds uniformly until **spherulites** come in contact with each other. The subsequent growth is then distorted and with these spherulites on the outside edge Grigorev's geometrical selection principles occur so that the lower nucleated spherulites are prevented from growing further (Fig.9.2b). These observations also apply to the rosette structure. The long fibrous form takes over and crystallisation continues at a constant rate and where opposing fibres meet they produce a common crystallisation line (BC in Fig. 9.2c) . The almost invisible banding that is common in some

Fig. 9.2 A crystallisation sequence starting from a silica gel precursor.

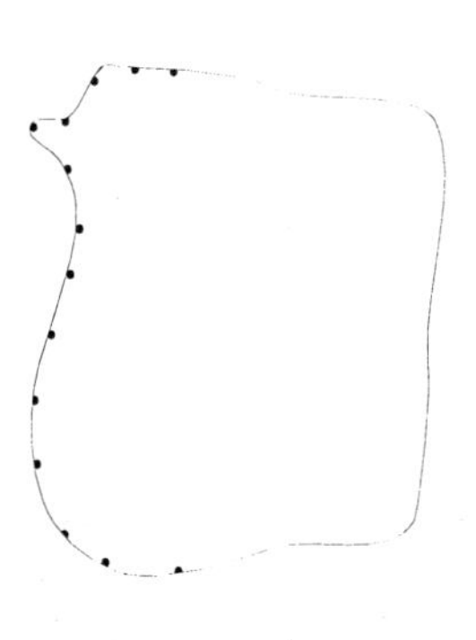

a)
Nuclcation starts from the outside edge.

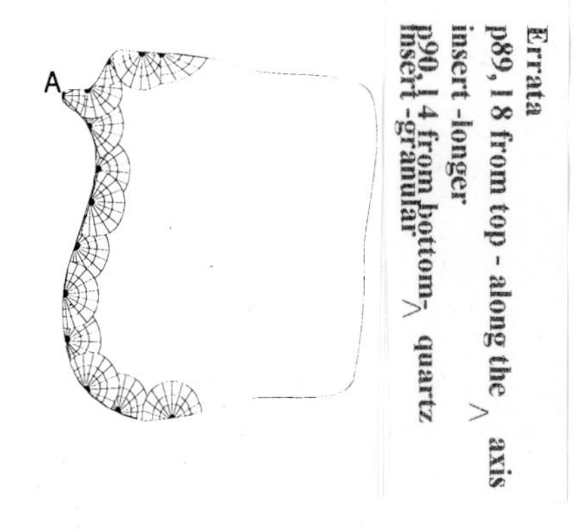

Errata
p89, l 8 from top - along the ^ axis
insert -longer
p90, l 4 from bottom- ^ quartz
insert -granular

b)
Lower spherulite (A) is eliminated.

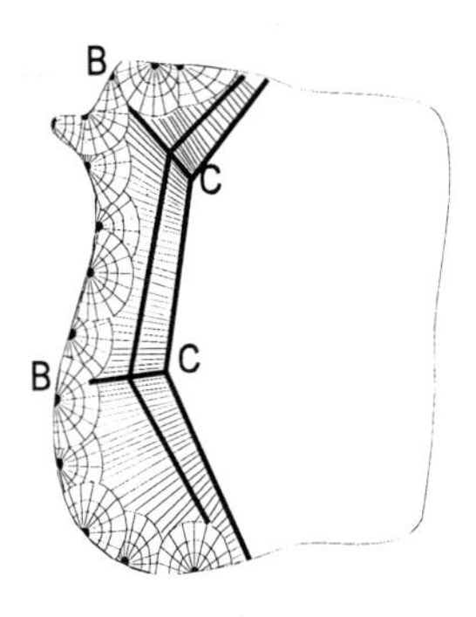

c)
The long fibrous form takes over and where opposing fibres meet they form a common crystallisation line BC.

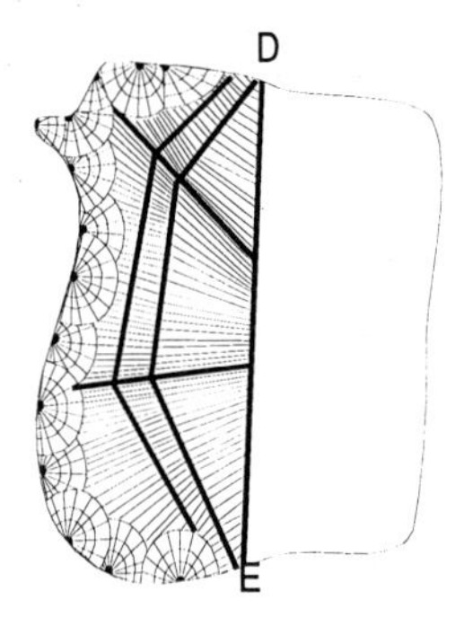

CdF

d)
The growth continues to the centre DE.

types of Midland Valley agate appear to represent pauses in the crystallisation process. The continuous banding reproduces the shape of the cavity wall but as the centre is approached, minor indentations in the outer edge become smoothed out in the later banding.

When the agate is approximately spherical or cylindrical, the fibre growth continues in all directions and finally meets the centre. A distorted ellipsoid or pear drop shape is more typical and the growth to the centre along the axis influences the fibre direction along the shorter axis. More elongated shapes allow fibrous sectors to become eliminated by geometrical selection.

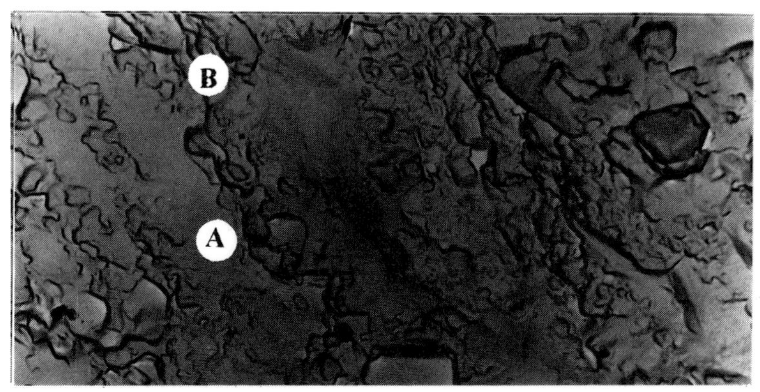

Fig. 9.3 TEM of clear chalcedony, Tayport. Short edge represents 19 μm. (x 2 800).

Quartz centres can be found in the iron-free agates from the eastern half of the Midland Valley. Transmission and scanning electron micrographs show a possible crystallisation sequence. The spherulitic fingers 'A' seek out the higher polymeric acids and crystallise as the flat areas of about 1 **μm**; quartz grains and bubbles are relatively few within these areas (Fig.9.3). Trace water and the lower polymeric acids are being pushed along the crystallisation front and also rejected into the troughs 'B'. The presence of the lower polymeric acids in the troughs enables the larger quartz crystals to grow. When the crystallisation front allows band formation the petrographic fibrosity ceases; this is perhaps due to an increase in the crystallisation rate. This increased crystallisation rate enables the petrographic hatched band to capture some of the water as small bubbles approximately 0.02 μm in diameter and at a density of

$30/\mu m^2$. In addition, larger bubbles around 0.3 μm in diameter are enclosed. Both white and blue-white bands have this common plate-like structure that is responsible for the brown colour when viewed in transmitted white light. The small 0.02 μm bubbles are responsible for the colour in the blue-white bands when viewed in **reflected** light.

Fig. 9.5 shows an agate with a quartz and amethyst centre. It is unusual in that the repeating **fortification** pattern does not approximate to the shape and form of the vesicle wall. One third of the length of the longer axis is clear chalcedony to be followed by twenty blue-white bands alternating with clear chalcedony for a distance of 2 cm. The same twenty bands are compressed into 2 mm along the shorter axis. It is problematical why the overall crystallisation rate along the long axis should be faster than along the short axis but as soon as the central area is approximately circular, quartz has started to form.These quartz crystals are typical of those found at the centre of agate: initially saccharoidal crystals are showing transitional fibrous structures reminiscent of chalcedony. These are part of the newly formed quartz crystals. When the crystals become elongated, feathery strain effects can be observed in polarised light and as the centre is approached the crystal grains increase in size. Where zoning is observed, there is evidence that the crystals have grown to an appreciable size, 0.04 mm, before settling and then continuing to grow.

Oehler (1976) found that the rate of growth of quartz from a silica gel had an initial linear rate that possibly corresponds to the growth of fibrous spherulites. The later non-linear kinetics could relate to the euhedral quartz crystals. Such a suggestion is compatible with chalcedony forming from a high viscosity gel while the quartz forms in the remaining relatively dilute solution. This proposition could equally apply to the formation of micro and macro quartz in agate geodes. If the crystallisation front rejects the water, a point will be reached where there is sufficient water from which quartz can crystallise.

The iron containing agates appear to be of two types: in the first case, the iron oxide makes up the band or is deposited as broken layers between the bands. A mechanism for the deposition of iron oxide would be an

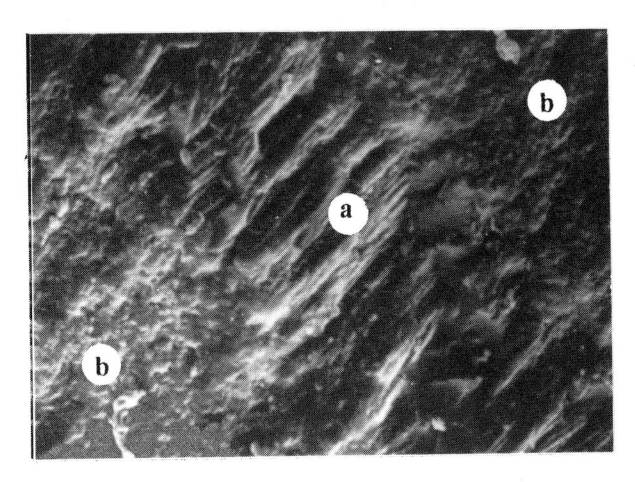

Fig.9.4 The white band (a) consists of the plate-like structures that contrast with the clear region (b). Botswana. Short edge represents 31 μm.(SEM, x 1 900).

Fig. 9.5 Amethyst, quartz and agate geode. Different rates of crystallisation have occurred along the long and short axes, Blackbank Farm, Perthshire. Actual size.

extension of the argument for the rejection of water in the pure silica type of agate. The two impurities, in this case, iron oxide as well as low polymeric silicic acid and water are driven along before the crystallisation front and, as suggested by Jessop (1930) would reach saturation levels at different times. Given an even but small distribution of water and iron oxide throughout the gel, the now out of phase iron oxide deposits would continue to be formed rhythmically and with regular band widths. Irregularities can be explained by variations in the rate of crystallisation. When the iron oxide is present in uneven patches , then such areas would be pushed along the front to be deposited as apparently broken bands. More difficult to explain are the second type that consist of initial banded areas evenly scattered with hematite spots followed by a central area apparently iron- free. Such agates could be the result of the crystallisation from an immiscible mixture of iron free and iron containing silica gels that have entered the vesicle simultaneously. Complex and fortification patterns have been reproduced by such a mechanism in gels and described in Chapter 5. Crystallisation would then proceed and the coarse texture of the iron containing areas eventually contrast with the finer morphology of the iron-free areas.

9.2 Final thoughts

The *Inflow Theory* has too many objections to provide an acceptable mechanism for agate genesis. However, the high temperature hypothesis is also speculative. Major problems include the requirement of a high density silica gel and the failure to detect any evidence of a chemical reaction between calcite and silica at these temperatures.

Interest in self organisation systems has prompted theoretical research into mineral banding (Fisher and Lasaga,1981; Wang and Merino, 1990 and others). However, the problems of agate genesis will only be entirely solved when the final stages of magmatic crystallisation are better understood. Detailed band analysis, investigations of the glassy lava residuum, continued studies on the fibrous structure are all aspects that will profit from further work and add to the fascinating story of agate genesis.

Nacken's (1948) comment,

there are still many questions to be answered,

continues to be true in 1996.

REFERENCES

BAUER, M. (1904): Precious Stones. *Griffin and Co.* Reprinted 1970.
BIRKS, L.S., SCHULMAN, J.H. (1950): The effect of various impurities on the crystallization of amorphous silicic acid. *Am. Min.* **35**, 214-217.
BLANKENBURG, H-J., BERGER, H. (1981):Kristallitgrössenuntersuchung-en an Vulkanitachaten. *Chem Erde.* **40**, 139-145.
BLANKENBURG, H-J., PILOT, J., WERNER, C-D. (1982): Erste Ergebnisse der Sauerstoffisotopenuntersuchungen an Vulkanitachaten und ihre genetische Interpretation. *Chem. Erde.* **41**, 213-217.
BLANKENBURG, H-J., SCHRÖN, W., STARKE,R., KLEMM,W. (1983): Beziehungen zwischen Achat, Jaspis und der Gesteinsmatrix in sauren Vulkaniten. *Chem Erde.* **42,** 157-172.
BRAITSCH, O. (1957): Über die natürlichen Faser-und Aggregationstypen beim SiO_2,ihreVerwachsungen,Richtungsstatistik und Doppelbrech- ung. *Heidelberger Beitr.Miner. Petrogr.* **5**, 331-372.
CARR, R.W., FYFE, W.S. (1958): Some observations on the crystallization of amorphous silica. *Am.Min.* **43,** 908-916.
COLLINI, C. (1776): Journal d'un voyage, qui contient differntes observations minéralogiques sur les agates et le basalte. After Liesegang, R.E. (1915).
CORWIN, J.F. (1958): Hydrothermal reactions under supercritical conditions V, J.Phys. Chem.**62**, 1086-1088.
CORWIN, J.F.,YALMAN, R.G., EDWARDS, J.W., OWEN, G.R.,SHAW, B.R. (1957):Hydrothermal reactions under supercritical conditions. I,II,IV. *J.Phys. Chem.* **61**, 939,941,1437.
DAVIES, S.N. (1964):Silica in streams and groundwater. *Am. J. Science.* **262,** 870-891.
DODGE, N.B. (1948):The dark field color immersion method. *Am. Min.* **33**, 541-549.
FARRINGTON, O.C. (1927): Agate-physical properties and origin. Dept of Geology, Field Museum of Natural History, Chicago. Leaflet No.8.
FALLICK, A.E., JOCELYN, J., DONELLY, T., GUY, M., BEHAN, C. (1985): Origin of agates in the volcanic rocks of Scotland. *Nature.* **313** , 672-674.
FISHER, G.W., LASAGA, A.C. (1981): Irreversible Thermodynamics in Petrology. In: Lasaga, A.C., Kirkpatrick, R.J. (eds) Kinetics of Geochemical processes. Reviews in Mineralogy. **8.** Min.Soc. Am.
FISCHER, W. (1954): Zum Problem der Achatgenese. *N. J. Miner. Abh.* **86**, 367-392.
FLÖRKE, O.W., KÖHLER-HERBETZ, B., LANGER, K., TÖNGES, I. (1982): Water in microcrystalline quartz of volcanic origin: Agates. *Contrib.Mineral. Petrol.***80,** 324-333.
FLÖRKE, O.W., GRAETSCH, H., MARTIN, B., RÖLLER, K., WIRTH,R., (1991): Nomenclature of micro and non-crystalline silica minerals, based on structure and microstructure. *N. Jb. Miner. Abh.* **163,** 19-42.
FOLK , R.L., PITTMAN, J.S., (1971): Length slow chalcedony: A new testament

for vanished evaporites. *J. Sed. Pet.*41, 1045-1058.
FOLK, R.L., WEAVER, C.E. (1952): A study of the texture and composition of chert. *Am. J. Science.* **250**, 498-510.
GANEYEV, I.G.(1975): Structure and properties of silicate melts. *Geochem. International,* **11**, 2, 329-337.
GRAETSCH,H. (1994): Structural characteristics of opaline and microcrystalline silica minerals. In Heaney, P.J., Prewitt,C.T., Gibbs, G.V., (eds) Silica. Reviews in Mineralogy. **29**. *Min.Soc.Am.*
GRAETSCH, H., FLÖRKE, O.W., MIEHE, G., (1985): The nature of water in chalcedony and opal-C from Brazilian agate geodes. Phys. Chem.Min. **14**, 300-306.
GRIGOREV, D.P. (1965): Ontogeny of Minerals, *Israel Programme of Scientific Translation , Jerusalem.*
HAIDINGER, W. (1849): Berichte über die Mittheilungen von Freunden der Naturwissenschaften in Wien. **65**,62-65, 118-119.
HARDER, H.(1993):Agates-formation as a multicomponent colloid chemical precipitation at low temperatures. *N. Jb. Miner. Mh.***1993,** H.1, 31-48.
HARDER,H., FLEHMIG,W. (1970): Quarzsynthese bei tiefen temperaturen. *Geochim. Cosmochim. Acta.* **34**, 295-305.
HARRIS, C. (1989): Oxygen-isotope zonation of agates from Karoo volcanics of the Skeleton Coast, Namibia. *Am. Min.* **74**, 476-481.
HEANEY, P.J. (1993); A proposed mechanism for the growth of chalcedony. *Contrib. Mineral. Petrol.* **115**, 66-74.
HEANEY, P.J., POST, J.E. (1992): The widespread distribution of a novel silica polymorph in microcrystalline quartz varieties. *Science.* **225**, 441-443.
HEDDLE, M.F. (1901): The Mineralogy of Scotland, vol 1, *David Douglas, Edinburgh.*
HEIN, H. (1908): Untersuchung über faserige Kieselsäuren und deren Verhältnis zu Opal und Quarz. *N. Jb. Miner. Geol. Palaont. Beil-Bd.*, 25, 182-231.After LIESEGANG, R.E. (1915).
HEIN, J.R., SCHOLL, D.W., BARRON, J.A., JONES, M.G., MILLER J. (1978): Diagenesis of late Cenozoic diatomaceous deposits and formation 155-181.
HEINZ, H. (1930): Die Entstehung der Achate, ihre Verwitterung und ihre künstliche Färbung. *Chem Erde.* **4**, 501-525.
HESSE, R. (1988):Origin of Chert, I. Diagenesis of biogenic siliceous sediments. *Geosci. Can.* **15**, (3) 171-192.
HEYDEMANN, A. (1964):Untersuchungen über die Bildungsbedingungen von Quarz im Temperatur bereich zwischen 100°C und 250°C. *Beitr. Mineral. Petrogr.* **10**, 242-259.
HOPGOOD, A.M., (1962): Radial distribution of soda in a pillow spilitic lava from the Franciscan, California. *Am.J. Science.* **260**, 383-396.
HUANG, W.H., KELLER,W.D. (1970): Dissolution of rock-forming silica minerals in organic acids: simulated first stage of weathering of fresh mineral surfaces. *Am. Min.* **55** , 2076-2094.

ILER, R.K. (1955):The Colloid Chemistry of Silica and Silicates. *CornellPress.*
ILER, R.K. (1979): Chemistry of Silica. *New York, Wiley Interscience.*
ISAACS, C.M. (1982): Influence of rock composition on kinetics of silica phase changes in the Monteray Formation, Santa Barbara area, California. *Geology* **10**, 304- 308.
ISEMURA, T. (1939): Studies on rhythmic precipitates. *Bull. Chem.Soc. Japan.* **14**, 179.
JESSOP, R. (1930): Agates and cherts of Derbyshire. *Geol. Assoc.*42, 29-43.
JONES, F.T., (1951): Iris agate. *Am. Min.* **37**, 578-587.
JONES, J.B., SEGNIT,E.R. (1971): The nature of opal I.Nomenclature and constituent phases. *J.Geol.Soc. Austral.* **18**, 17-51.
KAIBARA,H. (1964): A study of the microtexture of cherts. Me.Coll.Sci. Univ. Kyoto, Series B, 30, 59-73.
KEITH, H.D., PADDEN, F.J. (1963): Spherulitic crystallisation from the melt: II influence of fractionationation and impuritysegregation on the kinetics of crystallisation. *J.Appl. Phys.* **35**,1286-1296.
KEITH, H.D., PADDEN, F.J. (1964a): A phenomological theory of spherulitic crystallisation. *J.Appl. Phys.* **34** ,2409-2421.
KEITH, H.D., PADDEN, F.J. (1964b): Spherulitic crystallisation from the melt: I.fractionationation and impurity segregation and their influence on crystal morphology. *J.Appl. Phys.* **35**, 1270- 1285.
KNAUTH, L.P. (1994): Petrogenesis of chert. In : Heaney, P.J., Prewitt, C.T., Gibbs,G.V. (eds)) Silica. Reviews in Mineralogy, **29**. *Min. Soc. Am.*
KNOLL, H. (1942): Zur Anwendung der Liesengangschen Achattheorien. *Kolloid. Zeit.* **101**, 296-300.
KRAUSKOPF, K.B., BIRD, D.K. (1995): Introduction to Geochemistry. *McGraw Hill.*
LANDMESSER,M. (1984): Das Problem der Achatgenese. *Mitt POLLICHIA.* **72,** 5-137.
LANDMESSER, M. (1988): Transport -und Akumulationsmechanism des SiO_2 in petrolgischen Systemen: Achate. *Z. Dt. Gemmol. Ges.*,**36**. 3/4, 101-119.
LANDMESSER, M. (1992): Zur Geothermometrie und Theorie der Achate.- *Mitt POLLICHIA.* **79**, 159-201
LANGE,P., BLANKENBURG, H-J., SCHRON, W.(1984):Rasterelectronmikro-skopische Untersuchungenan Vulkanachaten.*Z. geol. Wiss.* **12**, 669-683.
LASIUS, (1789): Beobachtungen uber des Harzgebirge. Erster Theil.Hannover. 269. After LINCK,
LIESEGANG R.E. (1915): Die Achate. Dresden Leipzig.
LIESEGANG R.E. (1931): Achat -Theorien. *Chem Erde,* **6** , 143-152.
LINCK, G., HEINZ,H. (1930): Ergebnisse der Arbeit des Herrn H. Heinz über die Achate. *Chem.Erde,* **4,** 526-528.
MACKENZIE, F.T., GEES, R. (1971): Quartz: Synthesis at earth surface conditions. *Science.***173**, 533-535.
MACPHERSON,H.G. (1989): Agates. *British Museum.*

MARSHALL, R.R. (1961): Devitrification of natural glass. *Bull. Geol. Soc. Am.* **72**, 1493- 1520
MIDGLEY, H.G.(1951): Chalcedony and Flint. *Geol. Mag.* **88**, 179-184.
MIZUTANI, S. (1966): Transformation of silica under hydrothermal conditions. Nagoya Univ. Earth Sci.,**14**, 56-89.
MIZUTANI, S. (1977): Progressive ordering of cristobolite in the early stages of diagenesis. *Contrib. Mineral. Petrol.* **61**, 129-140.
MONROE, E.A. (1964): Electron optical observations of fine grained silica minerals. *Am. Min.* **49**, 339-347.
MOREY, G.W., FOURNIER, R.C., ROWE, J.J. (1962): The solubility of quartz in water in the temperature interval from 25°C to 300°C. *Geochim. Cosmochim. Acta.* **26**, 1029-1043.
MOXON, T.J. (1991): On the Origin of Agate with Particular Reference to Fortification agate Found in the Midland Valley, Scotland. *Chem. Erde.* **51**, 251-260.
MOXON, T.J. (1996): The co-precipitation of Fe^{3+} and SiO_2 and its role in agate genesis. *N. Jb. Miner. Mh.***1996,** H. 1, 21-36.
MYKURA,W. (1961): The Lower Old red sandstone Igneous Rocks of the Pentland Hills.Bull.Geol. Survey, G.B. **16**, 131-155.
NACKEN, R. (1948): Über die Nachbildung von Chalcedon- Mandeln. *Natur und Volk.* **78**, 2-8.
NAVROT, J., SINGER, A. (1976):Geochemical changes accompanying basic igneous rocks- clay transitions in humid Mediterranean climates. *Soil Sc.* **121**, 337-345.
NABOKO, S.I., SILNICHENKO, V.G., (1957): Formation of silica gel on solfataras of the Golovnin volcano on Kunashir Island. *Geochemistry.* **3**, 253-256.
NOEGGERATH, J. (1849): Sendschreiben an den K K wirklichen Bergrath und Prof., Herrn Wilhelm Haidinger in Wien, über die Achat -Mandeln in den Melaphyren. *Verh. naturhist. Ver.preuss.Rheinlande und Westphalens.* **6**, 243-260.
OEHLER, J.H. (1976): Hydrothermal crystallisation of silica gel. *Geol.Soc. Am. Bull.* **87**,1143-1152.
OLDERSHAW,A.E. (1968):Electron microscope examination of Namurian bedded cherts, North Wales. *Sedimentology.* **10**, 255-272.
OSTWALD,W. (1897): Lehrbuch der allgemeinen Chemie.778, Engelman, Leipzig. After STERN,K.H. (1954)
PELTO, C.R. (1956): A study of chalcedony.*Am.J. Science.* **254,** 32-50.
PETTIJOHN,E.J. (1975): Sedimentary Rocks. *Harper &Row.*
PILIPENKO, P.P. (1934): Zur Frage der Achat genese. *Bull. Soc.Natural. Moscou.geol Sect.* **12,** 279-299
PISCIOTTO, K.A. (1981): Diagenetic trends in the siliceous facies of the Monteray shale in the SantaMariaregion.California. *Sedimentology* 28, 547-571.
PITTMAN, J.S. (1959):Silica in Edwards Limestone, Travis County, Texas.. *Soc.Econ.Paleo.Min.*Spec. Pub. **7**, 121-134

REIS, O.M. (1916/17): Einzelheiten über Bau und Entstehung von Enhydros, Kalzitachat und Achat. *Geog. Jahresh.I.* **29/30**, 81-298.
RICHEY, J.E., (1961): Scotland: The Tertiary Volcanic Districts, British Regional Geology, *HMSO.*
SCHLOSSMACHER, K. (1950): Die Entstehung der Achate. *Schmuck und edles Gerät.* 23-26.
SCHUBEL, K.A., SIMONSON, B.M. (1990): Petrography and diagenesis of cherts from Lake Magadi, Kenya. *J. Sed. Pet.* **60**, 5, 761-776.
SIEVER, R. (1962): Silica solubility 0-200°C and the diagenesis of siliceous sediments. *J.Geol.* **70**, 127-156
SUNAGAWA, I., OHTA, E. (1976): Mechanism of formation of chalcedony. *Tohoku Univ. Sci. Report. Series* 3, **13**, No2, 131-146.
SMITH, J. (1910): Semi- precious stones of Carrick. *Cross Kilwinning*
STERN, K.H., (1954): The Liesegang Phhenomenon. Chem.Revs. **54**, 79-99.
TEDROW, J.C.F., WILKERSON, A.S. (1953):Weathering of glacial soil material.*Soil Science.* **75**, 345-353.
TYRELL, G.W. (1913): A petrographical sketch of the Carrick Hills. *Trans. Geo.Soc. Glasgow.* **15**, 64-83.
von BUCH, L. (1824): in von LEONHARD'S *Mineralogisches Taschenbuch für das Jahr 1824.* After NOEGGERATH (1849).
WALKER, G.P.L. (1960): The amygdale minerals in the tertiary lavas of Ireland. III. Regional Distribution. *Min.Mag.* **32**, 503-527.
WANG, Y., MERINO, E.(1990):Self-organizational origin of agates: Banding, fiber twisting, composition, and dynamic crystallization model.- *Geochim. Cosmochim. Acta.***54**, 1627-1638.
WHITE, D.E.(1955): Thermal springs and epithermal ore deposits. *Econ.Geol.* **50th Anniversary vol.** 99-154.
WHITE, D.E., BRANNOCK, W.W., MURATA, K.J. (1956): Silica in hot spring waters.*Geochim. Cosmochim. Acta.* **10**, 27-59.
WHITE, J.F., CORWIN, J.F. (1961): Synthesis and origin of chalcedony. *Am.Min.* **46**, 112-119.
WHITE, J.F.,SHAW.E,R,.CORWIN., J.F. (1958): A chalcedony-like variety of germania. *Am.Min.* **43**, 580-584.
WHITFORD-STARK,J.L., (1973): Vesicles and related structures in lavas. *Geol.J* .**8**, 2 317-332.
WRAY,D. A., (1948): The Penines and Adjacent Areas. British Regional Geology.*HMSO.*

AUTHOR INDEX

Appendix

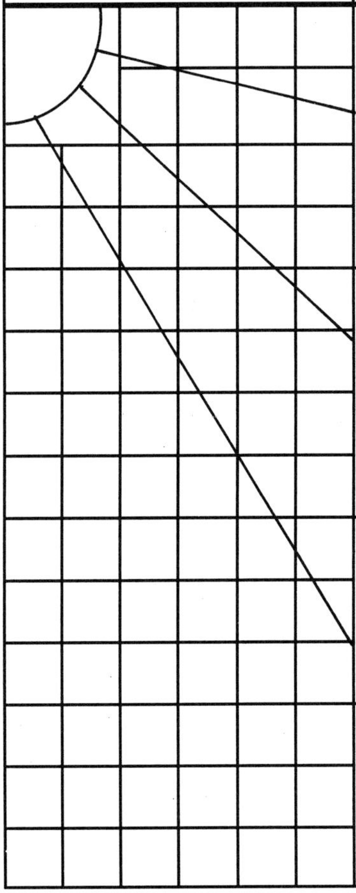

Thickness /mm 0.01 0.02 0.03 0.04 0.05	Order	Colour	Mineral
	1st	grey	
		white	quartz/ gypsum
		yellow	
		red	
	2nd	purple/blue	
		green	
		yellow	augite
		red	
	3rd	blue	
		green	
		rose	
	4th	pale green	
		pale pink	calcite
		paler green	

Diagnostic interference colours are observed when minerals are ground down to transparency and examined under crossed polars. The colours depend upon the nature and thickness of the mineral. Standard thickness is 0.03 mm and the colours shown by that mineral could include all, up to the maximum, for that particular mineral. The colours are not of equal intensity: second order colours are bright and pure; third order are similar in range but paler; fourth order are of a distinct pastel shade.

Separate coloured Birefrigence Charts can be purchased cheaply from:
Geo Supplies 16 Station Rd, Chapeltown, Sheffield (01142 403405)

Glossary

alkali. Substances that react with water and produce a pH > 7
alkali metal. The metals sodium, potassium are very reactive and will react with water to make a strong alkaline solution. Their compounds are amongst the most abundant in the earth's crust.
alkaline earth metal. Magnesium and calcium produce weak alkaline solutions and their compounds are widely dispersed in rocks.
amorphous silica. The non crystalline form of silica.
amygdale. The mineral filled gas cavity that is found in igneous rocks. Empty cavities are called vesicles.
andesite. A fine-grained igneous rock with slightly more silica than basalt.
augite. A calcium, magnesium silicate found in igneous rocks.
basalt. A fine-grained often glassy igneous rock that is low in silica.
biogenic. A term used for material produced by the action of living organisms.
Carboniferous. One of the geological periods that extends from 345 to 280 million years ago.
celadonite. A clay, mica-like mineral that is formed under low temperature conditions and found as a cavity infilling. It is often referred to as green earth because of its bright green colour.
chalcedony. A variety of quartz that is usually colourless to white and only shows its fibrous crystallinity when viewed under a polarising microscope.
chert. A microcrystalline variety of silica that is formed in a sedimentary environment. It forms as nodules or bands that are usually biogenic in origin.
chlorite. A group name for minerals that are layered silicates, usually green in colour.
conchoidal. A curved fracture pattern that is produced by broken glass or glassy minerals.
Cretaceous. One of the geological periods that extends from 145 to 65 million years ago.
Devonian. One of the geological periods that extends from 408 to 362 million years ago
diagenesis. The process of alteration that occurs, at low temperatures and pressures, in sedimentary rocks.
electrons. A sub-atomic particle of negligible mass that has a unit negative charge.
feldspar. The major group of rock forming silicate minerals. They are divided into the potassium, sodium, calcium and very rare barium feldspars.
ferromagnesian. A term used to describe the dark minerals in igneous rocks and refers to iron and magnesium silicates.
flocculation. A term used to describe the precipitation of fine particles from a solution.
fortification. A term that describes the most common banding pattern in agate.

The pattern produces onion-like layers in an effect that is reminiscent of the plan view of a castle.
geode. A hollow body that has quartz crystals or agate as a lining. The crystals grow unimpeded towards the centre of the cavity.
goethite. A yellow, oxy hydroxide iron ore.
gypsum. The hydrated form of calcium sulphate that is formed as an evaporitic mineral.
hematite. A mineral (iron(III) oxide) that is a major iron ore and responsible for the red colour in soil.
hydrothermal. The name given to processes that involve superheated water. At these high temperatures the steam is capable of breaking down rocks, including silicates.
igneous rock. A major rock group that is formed from a silicate melt.
inclusion. A sample of one substance that has been enclosed within another.
incongruent dissolving. The process whereby the dissolved substance converts into new substances.
infiltration canal. A peculiar banding feature that is found in certain types of agate. Various authorities have argued that the canal could allow either the entry or exit of silica solutions.
interference colours. When minerals are made into thin sections and viewed through crossed polaroids the crystal grains produce a variety of spectral colours.
ions. An atom or group of atoms that has either lost or gained electrons.
isotopes. These occur when elements, with the same atomic number, have atoms with different numbers of neutrons.
macroquartz. A term used to describe quartz crystals that are visible with the naked eye.
magma. A molten fliud that is found within the upper mantle of the earth.
magnetite. An important iron ore that is also sometimes found as a dust within igneous rocks.
micrometre. (μm). A unit of length. $1\ \mu m = 10^{-6}$ m.
microquartz. Quartz crystals that are below the limit of vision with the naked eye and require the use of a microscope.
mole. The concept is used to count elementary particles: electrons, ions, atoms, molecules. The number of particles that are present in a mole is 6×10^{23}.
mudstone. A clay- bearing rock that is lacking sedimentary banding.
opal. A silica mineral that is amorphous and found in fissures particularly near geysers and hot springs. The **-A** denotes the biogenic form of opal; while opal-**A'** is sometimes used to describe the inorganic type. When X-ray diffraction shows peaks of cristobalite and tridymite the opal is known as opal-**CT**.
orogenic. A process that is linked to the major mountain building periods in the earth's history. The processes can last for millions of years.
orthopyroxene. A series of chain silicate minerals that are found in igneous

rocks.
osmosis. The movement of water or solvent from a region of low concentration to one of higher concentration through a semi permeable membrane.
pegmatite minerals. The term describes minerals that are formed from hydrothermal solutions after the crystallisation of granitic rocks.
petrographic fibrosity. Crystalline fibres that can be observed in thin section when viewed down a polarising microscope.
pH. A scale from 0 to 14 that is used to indicate acidity, alkalinity or neutrality. The lower the value, the greater the acidity. A pH of 7 indicates a neutral solution.
phenocrysts. The first formed crystals in an igneous rock that are often large enough to be seen with the naked eye.
polymerisation. The process whereby single molecules repeatedly combine to produce new larger molecules.
Precambrian. The longest period of geological time that began at the formation of the Earth's crust (4 600 million years ago) and ended approximately 600 million years ago.
pyroclastic. Volcanic rocks that consists of fragmented particles.
refractive index. When light travels from air into a substance its velocity is reduced. The light path is refracted into the substance. The relationship between the angle of incidence (i) and the angle of refraction (r) is a constant given by Snell's law. The refractive index = sin i /sin r.
saturation. A saturated solution is one that contains the maximium amount of dissolved solute at that particular temperature.
silica gel. A thick jelly-like mass is formed when an alkaline silicate solution is neutralised by acid. The gel can also exist as smaller flocs.
silicic acid. The simple molecule H_4SiO_4 is the form of silica that exists in true solution. At near saturation, silicic acid can polymerise and then exists as dimers or trimers.
sol. A dispersion of small solid particles in a liquid.
spherulites. A term to describe fibrous growths that radiate from a single point. In agate they are usually less than 1 mm in diameter.
thin section. A slice of rock that has been ground down to the standard thickness of 0.03 mm.
undulatory extinction. This can appear when a bent crystal is viewed down the polarising microscope. Undulose extintion appears as a series of bands of darkness as the crystal is rotated with the polars in the crossed position.
vesicles. An empty gas cavity in volcanic rock.
xenolith. An inclusion of a pre-existing rock within an igneous rock.

INDEX